RANDOM HOUSE
ON

Literature

Collection 4

by Burton Goodman

Project Editor: Sandra Kelley
Production Supervisor: Lenore Zani
Design and Illustration: Educational Graphics,
   Inc. and Taurins Design Associates
Cover Design: Taurins Design Associates

International Standard Book Number:
   0-676-35632-X
Manufactured in the United States of America

Acknowledgments

Grateful acknowledgment is made to the following authors, agents, and publishers for permission to reprint these copyrighted materials:

"Thank You, M'am" by Langston Hughes reprinted by permission of Harold Ober Associates Incorporated. Copyright © 1958 by Langston Hughes. Copyright renewed 1986 by George Houston Bass.

"Ride a Wild Horse" by Hannah Kahn © 1953 Saturday Review magazine. Reprinted by permission.

"I Have Shaken Hands with a Great Many Friends" by Chief Joseph originally printed in Nimrod Vol. 16, No. 2, 1972, "American Indian Issue" as adapted by Francine Ringold from "An Indian's View of Indian Affairs," North American Review, Vol. 128, 1879, p. 432.

"Abraham Lincoln's Boyhood" adapted from ABRAHAM LINCOLN: THE PRAIRIE YEARS by Carl Sandburg, copyright 1926 by Harcourt Brace Jovanovich, Inc.; renewed 1954 by Carl Sandburg. Reprinted by permission of the publisher.

"I Have a Dream" by Martin Luther King, Jr. Reprinted by permission of Joan Daves. Copyright © 1963 by Martin Luther King, Jr.

"Lineage" from FOR MY PEOPLE by Margaret Walker. Published by Yale University Press, 1942. Copyright © by Margaret Walker. Reprinted by permission of the author.

"The Monkey's Paw" by W. W. Jacobs reprinted by permission of The Society of Authors as the literary representative of the Estate of W. W. Jacobs.

"The Rocking-Horse Winner" from THE COMPLETE SHORT STORIES OF D. H. LAWRENCE, VOL. III by D. H. Lawrence. Copyright 1933 by the Estate of D. H. Lawrence. Copyright renewed © 1961 by Angelo Ravagli and C. M. Weekley, Executors of the Estate of Frieda Lawrence Ravagli. Reprinted by permission of Viking Penguin, Inc.

Every effort has been made to trace the ownership of all copyrighted material in this book and to obtain permission for its use.

The following stories included in this book have been adapted by Burton Goodman: "The Luck of Roaring Camp," "Thank You, M'am," "Hospital Sketches," excerpt from Life on the Mississippi, "Abraham Lincoln's Boyhood," "The Monkey's Paw," "The Pardoner's Tale," "The Rocking-Horse Winner," and "Midas and the Golden Touch."

Table of Contents

unit 1
Turning Points

The great thing is to live, you know—to feel, to be conscious of one's possibilities.

—Henry James

The Luck of Roaring Camp

Bret Harte

Slowly the men became aware of beauty and meaning in the things around them.

There was commotion in Roaring Camp. It was not a fight. In those days of 1850, a fight would not have been noticed. The miners stopped working on their claims. The gamblers put down their cards. And you remember these were the same men who kept at their game the day that French Pete and Kanaka Joe shot each other to death.

The whole camp gathered in front of an old cabin. The men spoke in low voices. But they kept repeating one familiar name: "Cherokee Sal."

Perhaps the less said of her the better. Cherokee Sal was a sinful woman. But at the time, she was the only woman in Roaring Camp. Now, she was alone and in need and about to give birth.

So the men gathered in front of the cabin. Most were unmoved by her pain. But a few were touched by her suffering. Even Sandy Tipton said, "It sure is rough on Sal." For a moment, he ignored the fact that he had an ace up one sleeve and a knife up the other.

The situation was unusual. Deaths were not uncommon in Roaring Camp. But a birth there was a new thing. That was the reason for the excitement.

"You go in there, Stumpy," said a man named Kentuck. "Go in there and see what you can do. You've had experience in them things."

The talk was that Stumpy had a wife. In fact, they say he had two—at the same time. Since the people at

Roaring Camp didn't worry much about the law, Stumpy had found happy refuge there.

"You got a wife, Stumpy. You go in there."

Stumpy bowed wisely and entered the cabin. The door closed behind him. The men smoked their pipes and waited.

One hundred men waited. Some were outlaws. All were reckless. The strongest man had only three fingers on his right hand. The best shot had just one eye. As a group, they were frightening.

The camp lay in a valley between two hills and a river. The only way out was a steep trail over a hill by the cabin. This path was now lighted by the rising moon. The suffering woman might have seen it from the wooden bunk where she lay. It looked like a silver thread winding upward until it was lost in the stars above.

3

The night grew longer. Some of the men made a fire. They sat around it and laughed and joked. Bets were made. It was three to five that "Sal would make it through the night." It was even money that the child would live. Side bets were made as to the sex of the child.

Suddenly there came a cry from the cabin. It was a cry unlike anything ever heard before in the camp. The pine trees stopped moaning. The river ceased to rush. The fire stopped crackling. It seemed that Nature had stopped to listen, too.

The camp rose to its feet as one man!

"Let's explode a barrel of gunpowder!" someone shouted. But then, considering the mother's condition, it was decided to keep the noise down.

"Maybe just a few gunshots then," the man said.

The men fired into the air to mark the birth.

But Cherokee Sal was sinking fast. An hour later, Stumpy gave the news. "Boys," he said, "she has climbed the rugged road that leads to the stars." They understood by this that she was dead.

This did not upset the men too much, however. But they did worry about the fate of the baby.

"The child!" someone shouted. "Will he live?"

The answer was doubtful. The child needed milk. And the only other female around was a donkey.

Another hour passed. Finally, the

door to the cabin was thrown open. The men entered in single file. On a wooden bunk, they saw the figure of Cherokee Sal, covered by a blanket. Beside the bunk stood a pine table. On this was a cardboard box. In it, wrapped in red flannel, lay Roaring Camp's newest arrival. Near the box was a hat.

"Gentlemen," directed Stumpy, "please come in by the front door, pass around the table, and go out at the back. Them that wishes to leave a little something for the orphan will find a hat handy."

The first man entered with his hat on. As he looked at the baby, he removed his hat. Thus, everyone else followed his example. In a place like Roaring Camp, both good and bad actions are catching.

4

"Is that him?" someone whispered. "Mighty small fellow, ain't he?"

"Yeah," said another, "he ain't much bigger than a pistol."

As they circled the child, they left what they could in the hat. Each man gave the best he had to give: a silver tobacco box, a silver teaspoon, a revolver, a diamond ring, a sling shot, a Bible (giver not known), and about $200 in gold and silver coins.

Throughout the long procession, Stumpy remained silent.

As Kentuck bent over the box to look at the child, the baby turned. It reached up and grabbed Kentuck's finger. It held on tightly for a moment.

Kentuck looked foolish and embarrassed. His face turned bright red.

"Why the little cuss," he said. "He wrestled with my finger."

Kentuck held the finger apart from the others. He kept looking at it. "He wrestled with my finger," he kept repeating softly. "The d—d little cuss."

It was four o'clock in the morning before the men left. A light still burned in the cabin. Stumpy did not go to bed that night. Nor did Kentuck. He drank quite freely and kept repeating the story about the finger. "I tell you, Stumpy," he said over and over, "he wrestled with my finger."

5

After a while, Kentuck walked down to the river. Then he walked up toward the cabin, stopped at a large redwood tree, and walked back to the river. Then he hurried to the cabin and knocked on the door. It was opened by Stumpy.

"How goes it?" he asked, looking past Stumpy to the sleeping baby.

"All quiet," said Stumpy.

"Nothing new?" asked Kentuck.

"Nothing," replied Stumpy.

There was a long pause. Then Kentuck held up one finger. He smiled. "Wrestled with it," he said. "The little cuss." Then he went to bed.

The next day, the men found a spot on a hillside. After Cherokee Sal was put to rest, the camp held a meeting there. The question arose about what to do with the infant.

"Why, let's adopt it!" someone shouted.

"That's right," they agreed. "Let's adopt it!"

"Who'll take care of the baby?" asked Oakhurst the gambler.

That was a problem.

"Maybe we better send the child to Red Dog," suggested Tipton. "I hear that there are some females there."

This suggestion was shouted down. "This child belongs to Roaring Camp!" yelled Tom Ryder.

"What we need is a female nurse," someone said.

"Yes," was the answer. "But no decent woman would come to live at Roaring Camp."

"Right," said Oakhurst. "And we don't want no more of the other kind."

By this, he meant women like Cherokee Sal.

The men shook their heads. In the end, Stumpy spoke up. "I believe," he said softly, "I can bring up the child."

Shouts were heard. Hats were thrown into the air. This plan pleased the camp. They sent a messenger to Sacramento. "Buy what's needed," said the treasurer as he pressed a bag of gold dust into his hand. "Get the best that can be got. Lace and everything. Forget the cost!"

Strange to say, the child did well. Perhaps it was the mountain air. Perhaps it was the donkey's milk. Stumpy believed it was the good care the child was receiving. "Me and that donkey," Stumpy often said, "we been father and mother to him."

After a month, they decided it was time to give the baby a name. Until then he had been called "The Kid," or "Stumpy's Boy," or "the Coyote" because of how he yelled at night. Some called him by Kentuck's nickname, "the little cuss."

"He needs a real name," said Tipton.

"If you ask me," said Oakhurst the gambler, "this babe has brought 'the luck' to Roaring Camp."

Everyone agreed. The past month had been the best they ever had.

So "Luck" was the name agreed upon. For a first name, they called him Tommy.

"No man has a better right to be godfather than me," said Stumpy. No one argued. "We're here for a christening," he continued. "So let's have it." With that, he took the baby in his arms and said, "I proclaim you Thomas Luck, according to the laws of the United States and the State of California, so help me God."

From that moment, a change came over Roaring Camp. The cabin given to Tommy Luck—or "The Luck" as they called him—was papered and painted. It was kept perfectly clean. They bought a rosewood cradle which, as Stumpy said, "sorter killed the rest of the furniture." So fixing up the cabin became a necessity. Soon everyone began spending time at Stumpy's place.

To keep up with the competition, Tuttle's Grocery bought some carpets and mirrors. The mirrors made the men more aware of their clothing. And anyone who wished to hold The Luck had to have a clean shirt and a shaved face. Stumpy saw to that.

Someone said that noise was bad for Tommy. Shouting and yelling were no longer allowed. The men spoke in whispers. There was no more cursing. Singing, however, was seen as good for the baby and was permitted.

On long summer days, the men would take The Luck to work. They would place a blanket over the pine leaves. He would lie there while the men worked in the ditches. They would place flowers around the baby.

Sometimes they found bright pebbles in the creek. These they put aside as toys for Tommy. Slowly, the men became aware of beauty and meaning in the things around them. It was wonderful how many treasures the woods and hillsides held.

The baby seemed unusually content. Stories arose about him. "I crept up the bank," said Kentuck one day, "and guess what I saw. There was Tommy a-talkin' to a jay bird. It was a-sittin' on his lap. There they was, just as free with each other as you please. They was a-jawin' away just like two old friends."

It was the golden summer of Roaring Camp. They were wonderful times, for The Luck was with them. The mines yielded silver and gold. The men did well.

The camp kept to itself, no longer encouraging newcomers. Ready rifles kept strangers away. The only link with the outside world was the man who picked up the mail. This man sometimes told wonderful stories about Roaring Camp. He would say, "You should see the streets there. They've got vines and flowers around their houses. They wash themselves twice a day. They're mighty rough on strangers. And they worship a baby."

One day, sitting around a fire, Stumpy said, "We're doing pretty good. Might even say we're getting rich. Why don't we build a hotel here next spring? We could invite a decent family or two. It won't do for The Luck to grow up without no women folk."

The men talked it over. Outsiders and women! This was a new idea. Some of the men were against it. But then they thought about The Luck. They would do it for Tommy.

One or two still held out, of course. Secretly, they hoped that something might turn up.

And it did.

The winter of 1851 will long be remembered. The snow lay deep on the Sierras. Every mountain creek became a river. Every river became a lake. There was talk of floods. The town of Red Dog had been under water twice. They said Roaring Camp was next.

Then one night, the North Fork suddenly leaped over its banks. The water went rushing toward Roaring Camp. It swept away everything in its path. It tore down giant trees. Timbers broke. The darkness seemed to flow with the water and blot out the valley. Little could be done to save Roaring Camp.

When morning came, Stumpy's cabin had slipped into the river. They found Stumpy's lifeless body on higher land. But the pride—the hope —the joy—The Luck—of Roaring Camp had disappeared. With heavy hearts, the men walked back toward town. Just then, they heard shouts from below.

It was a rescue boat from down the river. They had picked up a man and an infant about two miles below. Did anyone know them? Did they belong here?

One look in the boat showed Kentuck lying there. He was badly crushed and bruised, but still holding The Luck of Roaring Camp in his arms. As they bent over, they saw the child was cold and lifeless.

"He is dead," someone said.

Kentuck opened his eyes. "Dead?" he asked weakly.

"Yes, my man, and you are dying, too."

A smile came into Kentuck's eyes. "Dying," he repeated. "He's a-takin' me with him. Tell the boys I've got The Luck with me now."

The strong man held tightly to the frail babe. He held him as a drowning man is said to cling to a straw. Kentuck closed his eyes. Then he drifted away into the shadowy river that flows forever to the unknown sea.

About the Author

Bret Harte (1836-1902)

Bret Harte was born in Albany, New York. He moved to California when he was nineteen years old. In San Francisco, he worked at a variety of jobs including teacher, miner, drugstore clerk, messenger, and printer. Finally, he got a position as assistant editor of a magazine. Later, he wrote a newspaper column.

When gold was discovered in California, Harte became fascinated by the change there. He began to write stories set in the new mining towns. These stories, noted for their freshness and local color, made Harte famous. "The Luck of Roaring Camp" is an excellent example of Harte's storytelling art.

Focus on the Story

A short story usually contains just one main idea. There are only one or two main characters in a short story. Short stories are considered fiction. This means that they tell about imaginary characters and events.

The **main character** of a story is the person the story is mostly about. A story may have more than one main character.

▶ **1.** The main characters in this story are _____ .

   a. Tommy Luck and Cherokee Sal
   b. Kentuck and Tommy
   c. French Pete and Kanaka Joe

The **plot** of a story is the outline of events. It is the action in the order in which it happened.

▶ **2.** Which of the following happened *last* in the plot of the story?
   a. The river overflowed its bank.
   b. Stumpy agreed to take care of the baby.
   c. Kentuck died.

The plot of a story is made up of episodes. An **episode** is an incident or an event in the story.

▶ **3.** What was the *first* episode in "The Luck of Roaring Camp"?
   a. A rescue boat appeared.
   b. Tommy Luck was born.
   c. Stumpy's cabin was washed away.

In many stories, the characters change. This change is called **character development.**

▶ **4.** Which word best describes the characters at the *beginning* of the story?
   a. reckless
   b. friendly
   c. well-dressed

A motive is the reason behind a character's action.

▶ **5.** At the end of the story, the men were different. What caused them to change?
   a. They struck it rich.
   b. They adopted a baby and wanted to set a good example.
   c. They rebuilt their town and no longer welcomed strangers.

Focus on the Language

A **simile** is a comparison that uses the words *like* or *as*.

Examples:
- The bread was as hard as a rock.
- She swims like a fish.

A **metaphor** is a comparison that does *not* use the words *like* or *as*.

Examples:
- He is a lamb.
- Her heart was a stone.

When a writer gives human traits to non-human things, this is known as **personification.**

Examples:
- The raindrops danced.
- The breeze whispered softly.

Many stories and poems contain **figurative language.** Figurative language is very descriptive, but it is not meant to be taken literally.

Examples:
- He was green with envy.
- They were frozen with fear.

▶ **1.** Below are three descriptions from "The Luck of Roaring Camp." Which one contains a simile?
a. The camp lay in a valley between two hills.
b. The path looked like a silver thread.
c. Every mountain creek became a river.

▶ **2.** Each of the following sentences describes Tommy Luck. Which one is a metaphor?
a. Tommy was happy.
b. He was as small as a pistol.
c. Tommy was the best gold mine that Roaring Camp had ever claimed.

▶ **3.** Which sentence contains personification?
a. The pine trees stopped moaning.
b. The river overflowed its banks.
c. There was talk of floods.

▶ **4.** At the end of the story, Kentuck "drifted away into the shadowy river that flows forever to the unknown sea." This means that Kentuck _____.
a. went aboard the rescue boat
b. began to swim down the river
c. died

Write About It

After the birth of Tommy Luck, a number of changes took place at Roaring Camp. Under the heading, "Changes at Roaring Camp," list these changes. Try to find at least five. The first one has already been done.

Changes at Roaring Camp

1. Tuttle's grocery bought carpets and mirrors.

Thank You, M'am

Langston Hughes

*The door was open. He could make a
dash for it down the hall. He could
run, run, run, run!*

She was a large woman with a large
purse. The purse had everything in it
but hammer and nails. It had a long
strap and she carried it slung across
her shoulder. It was about eleven
o'clock at night. She was walking
alone. A boy ran up behind her and
tried to snatch her purse. The strap
broke with the single tug the boy gave
it from behind. But the boy's weight,
and the weight of the purse combined,
caused him to lose his balance. Instead of taking off full blast as he had
hoped, the boy fell on his back on the
sidewalk. His legs flew up. The large
woman simply turned around. She
kicked him square in his blue-jeaned
sitter. Then she reached down and
picked the boy up by his shirt front.
She shook him until his teeth rattled.

After that the woman said, "Pick up
my pocketbook, boy, and give it here."

She still held him. But she bent
down enough to permit him to stoop
and pick up her purse. Then she said,
"Now ain't you ashamed of yourself?"

Firmly gripped by his shirt front,
the boy said, "Yes'm."

The woman said, "What did you
want to do it for?"

The boy said, "I didn't aim to."

She said, "You a lie!"

By that time, two or three people
passed. They stopped, turned to look.
Some stood watching.

"If I turn you loose, will you run?"
asked the woman.

"Yes'm," said the boy.

"Then I won't turn you loose," said
the woman. She did not let him go.

"Lady, I'm sorry," whispered the boy.

"Um-hum! Your face is dirty. I got a great mind to wash your face for you. Ain't you got nobody home to tell you to wash your face?"

"No'm," said the boy.

"Then it will get washed this evening," said the large woman. She started up the street, dragging the frightened boy behind her.

He looked as if he were fourteen or fifteen. He was thin. He wore tennis shoes and blue jeans.

The woman said, "You ought to be my son. I would teach you right from wrong. Least I can do right now is to wash your face. Are you hungry?"

"No'm," said the boy. "I just want you to turn me loose."

"Was I bothering *you* when I turned that corner?" asked the woman.

"No'm."

"But you put yourself in contact with *me*," said the woman. "If you think that that contact is not going to last awhile, you got another thought coming. When I get through with you, sir, you are going to remember Mrs. Luella Bates Washington Jones."

Sweat popped out on the boy's face. He began to struggle. Mrs. Jones stopped. She jerked him around in front of her and held him tight. She continued to drag him up the street. When she got to her door, she dragged the boy inside and down a hall. She led him into a large room at the back of the house. She switched on the light and left the door open. The boy could hear other people laughing and talking in the large house. Some of their doors were open, too. So he knew he and the woman were not alone. The woman still had him by the neck as they stood in the middle of her room.

She said, "What is your name?"

"Roger," answered the boy.

"Then, Roger, you go to that sink and wash your face," said the woman. Then she turned him loose—at last. Roger looked at the door—looked at the woman—looked at the door— *and went to the sink.*

"Let the water run until it gets warm," she said. "Here's a clean towel."

"You gonna take me to jail?" asked the boy, bending over the sink.

"Not with that face, I would not take you nowhere," said the woman. "Here I am trying to get home to cook me a bite to eat and you snatch my pocketbook! Maybe you ain't been to your supper either, late as it be. Have you?"

"There's nobody home at my house," said the boy.

"Then we'll eat," said the woman. "I believe you're hungry—or been hungry—to try to snatch my pocketbook."

"I wanted a pair of blue suede shoes," said the boy.

"Well, you didn't have to snatch *my* pocketbook to get some suede shoes," said Mrs. Luella Bates Washington Jones. "You could of asked me."

"M'am?"

The water dripping from his face, the boy looked at her. There was a long pause. A very long pause. He had dried his face. And not knowing what else to do, dried it again. Then, the boy turned around, wondering what next. The door was open. He could make a dash for it down the hall. He could run, run, run, *run*!

The woman was sitting on the day-bed. After a while she said, "I were young once and I wanted things I could not get."

15

There was another long pause. The boy's mouth opened. Then he frowned, not knowing he frowned.

The woman said, "Um-hum! You thought I was going to say *but*, didn't you? You thought I was going to say, '*but I didn't snatch people's pocketbooks.*' Well, I wasn't going to say that." Pause. Silence. "I have done things, too, which I would not tell you. Things I wouldn't tell God, if He didn't already know. Everybody's got something in common. So you set down while I fix us something to eat. You might run that comb through your hair. Then you will look presentable."

In another corner of the room behind a screen was a hot plate and an icebox. Mrs. Jones got up and went behind the screen. The woman did not watch the boy to see if he was going to run now. Nor did she watch her purse which she left behind her on the daybed. But the boy took care to sit on the far side of the room, away from the purse. There, he thought, she could easily see him out of the corner of her eye, if she wanted to. He did not trust the woman not to trust him. And he did not want to be mistrusted now.

"Do you need somebody to go to the store?" asked the boy. "Maybe to get some milk or something?"

"Don't believe I do," said the woman, "unless you want sweet milk yourself. I was going to make cocoa out of this canned milk I got here."

"That will be fine," said the boy.

She heated some lima beans and ham she had in the icebox. She made the cocoa and set the table. The woman did not ask the boy anything about where he lived. She didn't ask about his folks, or anything else that would embarrass him. Instead, as they ate, she told him about her job. She worked in a hotel beauty shop that stayed open late. All kinds of women came in and out, she said. Then she cut him a half of her ten-cent cake.

"Eat some more, son," she said.

Soon they were finished eating. She got up and said, "Now, here, take this ten dollars and buy yourself some blue suede shoes. And next time, do not make the mistake of latching on to *my* pocketbook *nor nobody else's.* Shoes got by devilish ways will burn your feet. I got to get my rest now. But from hereon in, son, I hope you will behave yourself."

She led him down the hall to the front door and opened it. "Good night! Behave yourself, boy!" she said, looking out into the street as he went down the steps.

The boy wanted to say something other than, "Thank you, m'am," to Mrs. Luella Bates Washington Jones. But although his lips moved, he couldn't even say that. He turned at the foot of the barren stoop and looked back at the large woman in the door. Then she shut the door. And he never saw her again.

About the Author

Born in Joplin, Missouri, Langston Hughes spent his boyhood in Kansas City, Colorado Springs, Buffalo, Cleveland, and Mexico. He wrote his first story as a high school assignment. From there, he went on to become one of this country's finest writers of poems, novels, and short stories.

Hughes's writing is noted for its deep concern for humanity. Much of it is sad, humorous, and touching. His poems have been translated into a number of languages, and many of them have been set to music. Hughes won many awards, including a Guggenheim fellowship.

Focus on the Story

The way an author shows what a character is like is called **characterization.** The way a person looks, talks, or acts is part of his or her characterization.

▶ **1.** Which of the following best characterizes Mrs. Luella Bates Washington Jones?
a. cruel and unfriendly
b. weak and shy
c. strong and loving

2. Which sentence best describes Roger?
a. He was short and heavy.
b. He was about fourteen and thin.
c. He was very well-dressed.

Dialogue is the speech between characters. Dialogue can help characterize the people in the story.

▶ **3.** Mrs. Jones said, "When I get through with you son, you are going to remember Mrs. Luella Bates Washington Jones." This line of dialogue shows that she _____.
a. was afraid of Roger
b. was going to have an important effect on Roger
c. believed that Roger would soon forget her

Motive

▶ **4.** Why did Roger try to steal the purse?
a. He needed the money to buy food.
b. He wanted to buy shoes.
c. He owed money to his friends.

The **setting** of a story is *where* the action takes place. The setting can also mean *when* the story happens.

▶ **5.** The setting of "Thank You M'am" is a _____.
a. city at the present time
b. city during the 1800s
c. country road in the 1970s

Focus on the Language

Synonyms are words that have the same or very similar meanings.

Examples:
- *Attempt* is a synonym for *try*.
- *Hurry* is a synonym for *rush*.

Antonyms are words that have opposite meanings.

Examples:
- *Fast* is an antonym for *slow*.
- *Large* is an antonym for *small*.

Homonyms are words that sound the same but are spelled differently and have different meanings.

Examples:
- *Knew* and *new* are homonyms.
- *Through* and *threw* are homonyms.

Talk It Over

▶ **1.** Mrs. Jones didn't ask about anything that would embarrass Roger. A synonym for *embarrass* is _____ .

a. *teach*
b. *help*
c. *make self-conscious*

▶ **2.** An antonym for *trust* is _____ .
a. *believe*
b. *doubt*
c. *ask*

▶ **3.** The weight of the purse caused Roger to fall. A homonym for *weight* is _____ .
a. *height*
b. *light*
c. *wait*

1. How did Mrs. Jones show Roger that it was important to trust people? What did she do to show Roger that she trusted him? What did Roger do to show her that he could be trusted?
2. At the end of the story, Roger wanted to say "Thank you" to Mrs. Jones. But he couldn't. Why not? Was there ever a time when you couldn't find the words to express how you felt?
3. Roger had never met anyone like Mrs. Jones before. She was a person who treated him with respect. She also demanded respect in return. What effect did their meeting have on Roger? Would Roger's life have been different if he had been raised by someone like Mrs. Jones? How does the way people are treated affect the way they act?

19

Ride a Wild Horse

Hannah Kahn

Ride a wild horse
with purple wings
striped yellow and black
except his head
which must be red.

Ride a wild horse
against the sky
hold tight to his wings . . .
Before you die
whatever else you leave undone,
once, ride a wild horse
into the sun.

Focus on the Poem

Poetry is a special use of language. A poem is meant to be heard—like a song. Listen to how the words sound. Think about the picture the poet creates.

Imagery is the picture that the poet creates in the mind of the reader. Unlike figurative language, imagery is meant to be taken literally.

▶ **1.** In the first part of this poem, a horse is described. What is unusual about this horse?
a. It has wings; it is yellow and black; and it has a red head.
b. It is wild; most horses are tame.
c. There is no one riding it.

A **symbol** is something that represents something else. In this poem, riding a wild horse stands for taking chances. Understanding a symbol can help you understand the meaning of the poem.

▶ **2.** When the poet says "ride a wild horse," what does she mean?
a. Find a horse of many colors.
b. Take a chance at least once in your life.
c. Write a poem about horses.

3. The line, "Hold tight to his wings," means that you should _____.
a. find a horse with wings
b. hold the reins tightly when you ride a horse
c. not let an opportunity go by

Synonym

▶ **4.** Which word is a synonym for *wild*?
a. *untamed*
b. *empty*
c. *mild*

Homonym

▶ **5.** A homonym for *die* is _____.
a. *live*
b. *perish*
c. *dye*

Unit Review

Write your answers on a separate sheet of paper.

1. In "The Luck of Roaring Camp," Stumpy decided to raise Tommy. This event is part of the _____ of the story.
   - **a.** plot
   - **b.** character development
   - **c.** dialogue

2. Each story in this unit showed the development of one or more characters. Which character changed the most?
   - **a.** Oakhurst
   - **b.** Stumpy
   - **c.** Mrs. Luella Bates Washington Jones

3. In "Thank You, M'am," Roger tried to grab Mrs. Jones's purse. This event was the first _____ in the plot.
   - **a.** episode
   - **b.** dialogue
   - **c.** setting

4. "Shoes got by devilish ways will burn your feet." This line of dialogue was spoken by _____ .
   - **a.** Roger to Mrs. Jones
   - **b.** Kentuck to Stumpy
   - **c.** Mrs. Jones to Roger

5. Match each term with its definition.
   - **a.** main character — where and when the action of the story takes place __
   - **b.** setting — the way a person looks, talks, or acts __
   - **c.** characterization — the person the story is mostly about __

Reviewing the Language

1. In "The Luck of Roaring Camp," Cherokee Sal "climbed the rugged road that leads to the stars." This figurative language means that _____ .

   a. Cherokee Sal climbed a tall mountain
   b. Cherokee Sal was planning to leave the camp
   c. Cherokee Sal died

2. Which sentence from "The Luck of Roaring Camp" contains a simile?

   a. They was a jawin' away just like two old friends.
   b. There was Tommy a-talkin' to a jay bird.
   c. He's a takin' me with him.

3. Match each sentence with the term that describes it.

   a. metaphor
   b. personification
   c. imagery

   The flood waters swallowed Roaring Camp. __
   Ride a wild horse with purple wings. __
   Mrs. Jones was a bear who protected a lost cub. __

4. Mrs. Luella Bates Washington Jones told Roger, "You ought to be my son." A homonym for son is _____ .

   a. *child*
   b. *sun*
   c. *daughter*

Talking It Over

1. This unit is called "Turning Points." Think about "The Luck of Roaring Camp," and "Thank You, M'am." What event in each story served as a "turning point"?

2. Mrs. Luella Bates Washington Jones allowed a criminal to go free. Why? Would anything have been gained if she had called the police?

3. In "Ride a Wild Horse," the poet says that people should take chances. What chance did Mrs. Jones take? What chance did Stumpy take? Did these characters gain anything by taking chances?

23

unit 2
Reflections of America

*We resolve . . . that
government of the people, by
the people, for the people shall
not perish from the earth.*

—Abraham Lincoln

From
Hospital Sketches

Louisa May Alcott

*Louisa May Alcott wanted to do some-
thing useful. Her brother suggested
she become a nurse. She volun-
teered. This is her account as she
worked at an army hospital during
the Civil War.*

December 3, 1862 Concord

I was determined to do something especially useful. Having made
this decision, I asked for suggestions.

"Write a book," said my father.

"I don't know enough," I answered. "First live, then write."

"Try teaching again," suggested my mother.

"No thank you, ma'am, ten years of that is enough."

"Be a nurse to the soldiers," said my young brother, Tom.

"I will!"

I know that the Union Hotel Hospital in Georgetown, D.C., is
accepting volunteers. I plan to arrange for an interview as soon as
possible. Should my request be accepted, I will leave at once.

December 13, 1862 Washington—Eleven P.M.

It was dark when we finally arrived in Washington. I do not find traveling by train extremely uncomfortable. Yet we were delayed due to an accident, for no journey in America would be complete without one. A coupling iron broke, and, after leaving the last car behind us, we waited for it to come up, which it did, with a crash that knocked everyone forward on their faces. Hats flew off, bonnets were flattened, the stove skipped, the lamps fell down, the water jar turned upside down, and the wheel just over which I sat received some damage. Of course, it became necessary for all the men to get out, and stand about in everybody's way, while repairs were made.

The country through which we passed did not seem so very unlike that which I had left except it was more level and less wintry. I'd often been told that Washington was a spacious place. Still, its size quite took my breath away. The Capitol was so like the pictures I had so often seen, that it did not overly impress me. The White House was lighted up, and carriages were rolling in and out of the great gate. How I longed to visit the famous East Room! Pennsylvania Avenue with its bustle, lights, and music made me feel as though I'd landed somewhere during Carnival time.

Meanwhile, it is growing late. My heart is beating rather faster than usual, as I am struck by the thought that I am very far from home, and tomorrow I begin my service at the hospital.

There they were! "Our brave boys!" as the papers rightfully called them. In they came, some on stretchers, some in men's arms, some feebly staggering along on crude crutches. Everywhere was hurry and confusion; the hall was full of the injured and hurt. Along the wall were rows of beds on which sat those who could manage. The floors were covered with the more seriously wounded. The steps and doorways were filled with helpers and lookers on.

The sight of several stretchers, each with its wounded soldier, reminded me that I was there to work, not to wonder or weep. So I held my feelings in check and went about my job.

Forty beds were prepared, many already claimed by tired men who fell down anywhere and slept till the smell of food awakened them. Round the great stove was gathered the dreariest group I ever saw—ragged, gaunt and pale, muddy to the knees, with bloody bandages untouched since they had been put on many days before. I pitied them so much, I dared not speak to them; yet I yearned to serve the dreariest of them all. Then began a long day of administration of medicines, washing feverish faces, smoothing tumbled beds, wetting and dressing wounds, and finally, in the evening, singing lullabies.

December 21, 1862

Since I am fond of the night side of nature, I was soon promoted to the post of night nurse. Another nurse relieved me at dawn, we two taking care of the ward between us. I tried to keep my boys in a jolly state of mind since it is a known fact that I believe that he who laughs most is surest of recovery.

Wherever the sickest or most helpless man chanced to be, there I kept my watch. Last night I stationed myself next to the bed of a New Jersey boy. He had become crazed by the horrors of war. A slight wound in the knee brought him to the hospital, but his mind had suffered more than his body. For days he had been reliving in his imagination the terrible scenes he could not forget. From time to time he would break out in screams pitiful to hear. As I sat by him, I tried to soothe his distracted brain by constantly placing wet cloths upon his hot forehead. After a while, he stopped cheering his comrades on. He ceased counting them as they fell around him. His eyes finally grew restful and he achieved, at last, a bit of peace in sleep.

About the Author

Louisa May Alcott (1832–1888)

Louisa May Alcott is best known as the author of *Little Women*. Her other novels include *Little Men* and *Jo's Boys*. Some of the characters she created—Jo, Beth, Amy, and Meg—are among the most loved in literature.

In 1862, Alcott worked for a period of time as a volunteer nurse at the Union Hotel Hospital in Georgetown, Washington, D.C. *Hospital Sketches* is based on her experiences there. It is a true account of life in an army hospital during the Civil War.

Focus on the Letters

The way an author feels about the subject matter is known as the **author's viewpoint**.

▶ **1.** In *Hospital Sketches*, Louisa May Alcott said that to write, one must "first live." Which of the following best expresses Alcott's viewpoint about writing?
a. It is very easy to be a writer.
b. Personal experiences provide a writer with subject matter.
c. It is harder to be a nurse than a writer.

2. According to Louisa May Alcott, traveling by train in 1862 _____ .
a. always went smoothly
b. was extremely uncomfortable
c. usually resulted in delays

3. Louisa May Alcott believed that _____ .
a. the Capitol didn't look like the pictures of it
b. there was no point in trying to help those soldiers who were in the worst condition
c. a happy state of mind helps a patient to recover

Focus on the Language

One way of finding the definition of a word is by using the dictionary. Another way is to see how the **word** is used in the sentence, or **in context**.

▶ **1.** What is the meaning of the word *distracted* in this sentence? Louisa May Alcott tried to soothe the distracted brain of the soldier who had been screaming.
a. troubled
b. pleased
c. relaxed

2. What is the meaning of the word *post* in this sentence? I was soon promoted to the post of night nurse.
a. a piece of wood
b. position or station
c. to place on a bulletin board

30

From
Life on the Mississippi

Mark Twain

---

*There's only one way to be a pilot,
and that is to know this entire river
by heart.*

When I was a boy, there was just one great dream among my friends in our village on the west bank of the Mississippi River. That was to be a steamboatman. We had other dreams, but they were only passing. When a circus came and went, it left us all burning to become clowns. Now and then, we thought we might be pirates. Those hopes faded, each in its turn. But the dream of being a steamboatman always remained.

Once a day, a ship arrived upward from St. Louis. Another arrived downward from Keokuk. Before these events, there was something to look forward to. After them, the day was dead and empty. Not only the boys, but the whole village, felt this. After all these years, I can still picture that old time to myself. I can see it now just as it was then.

I see the whole town dozing in the sunshine of a summer's morning. The streets are empty, or pretty nearly so. One or two clerks sit in front of the Water Street stores. Their chairs are tilted back against the walls. Their chins are on their necks, their hats pushed back over their faces. They are fast asleep. Here and there, pigs loaf along the sidewalk eating watermelon rinds and seeds.

On the stone wharf, there are piles of freight. The town drunkard lies asleep in the shadow of them. Nobody listens to the waves slapping peacefully against the wharf. The great Mississippi, the majestic, the magnificent Mississippi, rolls its mile-wide tide along, shining in the sun.

Soon, a film of dark smoke appears in the distance. A great cry goes up, "S-t-e-a-m-boat a-coming!" and the scene changes.

The town drunkard opens his eyes. The clerks wake up. In a twinkling, the dead town is alive and moving. Carts, men, boys pour out of every house and go hurrying to the wharf. There, the crowd gazes upon the coming boat as though it is a wonder they are seeing for the first time.

And the boat *is* rather a handsome sight, too. She is long and sharp and

trim and pretty. She has two tall, fancy chimneys and a pilot-house made of glass. There is a flag flying from the staff. The upper decks are filled with passengers. The captain stands by the big bell, calm, in command, the envy of all.

Now black smoke rolls and tumbles out of the chimneys. The deck-hand stands waiting, a coil of rope in his hand. The captain lifts his hand. A bell rings. The wheels stop, and the steamer is at rest.

There is a mad rush to get aboard and to get ashore, to load and to unload. The air is filled with the sounds of shouting. Ten minutes later, the boat is under way again. No flag flies from the staff. No black smoke comes from the chimney. After ten more minutes, the town is dead again. The town drunkard lies asleep once more.

My father was a justice of the peace. I guess he had the power of life and death over men. That was an important and respected job. But as for me, I wanted to be a steamboatman. First, I wanted to be a cabinboy. I wanted to come out with a white apron on and shake a tablecloth over the side, where all my friends could see me. Later, I thought I would rather be the deck-hand who waited with the coil of rope in his hands. No one could miss him.

But these were only day-dreams. They were too wonderful to be thought of as possible. Then, one of my friends went away. He was not heard of for a long time. At last, he showed up. He was an engineer's assistant on a steamboat! Whenever his boat was being repaired, he would hang around the town. He wore his blackest and greasiest clothes, so that no one could forget he worked on a steamboat. He used all sorts of steamboat talk, and told wonderful tales of the places he'd seen.

This fellow had money, too, and hair oil. He had a silver watch with a shiny brass chain. No youth was more admired, or envied, or hated than he. When his boat blew up, peace came to us all. But then he returned home the next week, all battered and in bandages, a shining hero for all to see.

This was too much. It brought about just one result. Boy after boy managed to "get on the river." The minister's son became an engineer. The doctor's and the postmaster's sons became "mud-clerks." The liquor dealer's son became a bartender on a boat. A few boys even became pilots. Pilot was the greatest job of all! Even in those days, they could make two hundred and fifty dollars a month! But some of the boys, like me, could not get on the river. Our parents wouldn't let us.

So, by and by, I ran away. I said I would never come home again until I was a pilot. I went down to the St. Louis wharf. I went aboard a few of the boats that lay packed together like sardines. I said I should like to learn to be a pilot. But I got a cold shoulder and harsh words from the mates and the clerks. For the time being, I had to make the best of this treatment. But I dreamed of a future when I should be a great and honored pilot, famous and with plenty of money.

Months later, I booked passage on an old boat called the *Paul Jones.* While aboard, I made friends with one of the pilots, Mr. Bixby. He taught me how to steer the ship. I had a plan. For three days, I begged him to teach me how to be a pilot. Finally he agreed. For five hundred dollars, he would teach me the Mississippi River from New Orleans to St. Louis. I would pay him later out of the wages I would make.

I thought "learning" thirteen hundred miles of the Mississippi would be easy. I thought that all a pilot had to do was keep his boat in the river. And I did not think *that* was much of a trick, since it was so wide. Had I known what really was required, I would not have had the courage to begin.

The boat backed out of New Orleans at four in the afternoon. It was "our watch" until eight. My pilot, Mr. Bixby, "straightened her up" and moved her alongside the other boats on the bank.

Then he said, "Here you take her." I took the wheel, and my heart began to pound wildly. It seemed to me we were about to scrape the side off every ship in the line, we were so close. I held my breath and began to steer the ship away from danger.

"No, no," screamed Mr. Bixby, "stay in line!" Then taking the wheel, he showed me how.

Now and then, Mr. Bixby pointed out certain things. He said, "This is Six-Mile Point." I nodded. It was pleasant enough information, but I could not see the use of it. It didn't interest me. Another time he said, "This is Nine-Mile Point." Later he said,

"This is Twelve-Mile Point." They were all about level with the water's edge. They all looked about the same to me. I hoped that Mr. Bixby would change this boring subject.

When our watch was ended, we had supper and went to bed. At midnight, the glare of a lantern shown in my eyes. The night watchman said, "Come, get up!"

Then he left. I could not understand why he had awakened me. I gave up trying to, and went back to sleep. Pretty soon, the watchman was back again. This time he was angry. I was annoyed. I said, "Why do you come around here bothering me in the middle of the night? Now I probably won't be able to fall asleep again."

The watchman said, "Well how do you like that! If this ain't good!"

The other "watch" was just turning in. I heard them laughing. Someone said, "Hey, watchman, be careful with him. He's delicate. Give him some sugar and have the maid sing, 'Rock-a-bye, Baby' to him."

Just about then, Mr. Bixby appeared. One minute later, I was climbing up the pilot-house steps. I had some of my clothes on and the rest in my arms. Mr. Bixby was close behind me, yelling in my ears. I knew that boats ran all night. But somehow I never thought that somebody had to get up out of a warm bed to run them. I began to fear that piloting was not quite as romantic as I had imagined.

It was rather a dark night, although a few stars were out. The mate was at the wheel. He had the boat pointed at a star and was steering it straight up the middle of the river.

He turned to Mr. Bixby and said, "We've got to land at the Jones plantation, sir."

I smiled to myself and thought, "I wish you luck, Mr. Bixby. You'll never find Mr. Jones' plantation on a night like this."

Then the mate left. I said nothing. But I was dying to ask Mr. Bixby how he was going to find that plantation on a night when every plantation looked exactly alike.

Mr. Bixby headed toward the shore. Soon he was riding alongside of it in the dark, just as if it had been daylight. Not only that, he was singing softly to himself.

After a while, he turned to me and said, "What's the name of the first point above New Orleans?"

I was glad to be able to answer at once. And I did. I said I didn't know.

"Don't *know*?"

His manner surprised me. But I had to say just what I had said before.

"Well, you're a smart one!" said Mr. Bixby. "What's the name of the next point?"

Once more, I didn't know.

"Well, this beats anything. Tell me the name of *any* point or place I told you."

I thought for a while and couldn't.

"What *do* you know?" he demanded.

"I—I—nothing for certain."

"By the great Caesar's ghost," he yelled, "I believe you! You're the stupidest dunderhead I ever saw or heard of. The idea of *you* being a pilot— *you*! Why, you don't know enough to pilot a cow down a path!"

Oh, but his anger was up. He was a nervous man. He shuffled from one side of the wheel to the other, as if the floor were hot. He would boil awhile to himself and then scream at me.

"Look here! What do you suppose I told you the names of those points for?"

I trembled for a moment before answering. "Well—to—to be entertaining, I thought."

This was like waving a red rag at a bull. He raged and stormed. He threw open a window and stuck out his head. There followed such a stream of curses as I had never heard before. Finally, he said to me very very softly, "My boy, you must get a little notebook. And every time I tell you a thing, put it right down. There's only one way to be a pilot, and that is to know this entire river by heart. You have to know it just like ABC."

This was sorry news to me. For my memory was never loaded with anything but blanks. After a while, Mr. Bixby pulled a rope and banged on the bell. The stars were all gone now, and the night was as black as ink. I could hear the wheels along the bank. But I could not see the shore. Then I heard the watchman calling from the upper deck.

"What's this, sir?" I asked.

"The Jones plantation," answered Mr. Bixby.

I said to myself, "I'll make a small bet that it isn't." But I said nothing. In a few moments, the boat's nose came to the land. A torch glowed. A man skipped ashore . . . and the next moment, we were heading up the river again.

I thought for a while. Then I said—but not aloud—"Well, finding that plantation was the luckiest accident that ever happened. It couldn't happen again in a hundred years!"

About the Author

Mark Twain (1835-1910) ⸻

Mark Twain was the pen name of Samuel Langhorne Clemens, one of the best-known and most-loved of all American authors. His novels, *The Adventures of Tom Sawyer* and *The Adventures of Huckleberry Finn* are considered classics of American literature.

Clemens spent his boyhood in Hannibal, Missouri, a town he later used as the setting for *Tom Sawyer*. After his father died, he left school to work as a printer. Clemens later set out for South America. However, he got no farther than New Orleans, where he met the famous steamboat pilot, Horace Bixby. With Bixby's help, he became a cub pilot, an experience he described in *Life on the Mississippi*. When Clemens began to write, he chose the name "Mark Twain." This is a river term which means "two fathoms deep."

Focus on the Autobiography

An autobiography is a type of literature in which a person tells about his or her own life. Autobiographies are classified as nonfiction. They tell about real characters and events.

In an autobiography, writers tell about their whole life or about an episode in their life.

▶ **1.** Which of the following is true of this selection from *Life on the Mississippi?*
a. It is about an episode in Mark Twain's life.
b. It is autobiographical.
c. both of the above

The person who tells the story is known as the **narrator.** Often, the narrator is one of the characters in the story.

▶ **2.** The narrator of this story is _____.
a. Mr. Bixby
b. Mark Twain
c. the watchman

Stories are told from a *first-person* or a *third-person* **point of view**. In the *first-person point of view*, a character tells the story, using the words *I* or *me*. In the *third-person point of view*, the author—acting as an observer—tells the story, using the words *he, she,* or *they.*

▶ **3.** From whose point of view is *Life on the Mississippi* told?
a. the first-person point of view
b. the third-person point of view
c. the point of view of a character not in the story

Characterization

▶ **4.** Which words best characterize Mr. Bixby?
a. impatient and skilled
b. kind and quiet
c. stupid and afraid

5. Which phrase best characterizes the narrator?
a. quick learner
b. good pilot
c. poor student

Focus on the Language

The repetition of consonant sounds is called **alliteration.**

Examples:
  • He *told* a *tale* of *terror.*
  • The *woods* are *wonderful* and *wild.*

Simile

When figurative language is used too often, it loses its power. An overused simile or metaphor is called a **cliché.**

Example:
  • He's as busy as a bee.

▶ **1.** Which sentence from *Life on the Mississippi* contains alliteration?
a. On the stone wharf there are piles of freight.
b. Pigs loaf along the sidewalk.
c. The majestic, the magnificent Mississippi rolls along.

▶ **2.** Following are three descriptions of the night. Which one contains a simile?
a. It was rather a dark night.
b. The night was as black as ink.
c. The stars were all gone.

▶ **3.** Which sentence contains an expression which is considered a cliché?
a. The town drunkard lies asleep in the shadows.
b. The boats were packed together like sardines.
c. Black smoke tumbles out of the chimneys.

Find Out More

Most libraries group their books according to a special plan. This plan is called the **Dewey Decimal System.** There are ten major classifications in this system. Within each classification, books are arranged by **call number.** To find a book on the library shelf, look for its call number which is printed on the spine. The box below shows the classification numbers.

THE DEWEY DECIMAL SYSTEM
000–099 General Works
100–199 Philosophy
200–299 Religion
300–399 Social Science
400–499 Language
500–599 Pure Science
600–699 Applied Science & Useful Arts
700–799 Fine Arts & Recreation
800–899 Literature
900–999 History, Geography, Biography

▶ **1.** Short stories are considered literature. In which book would you find a collection of short stories?

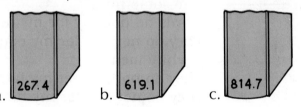

a. 267.4   b. 619.1   c. 814.7

2. Books of biography would be grouped between which of the following numbers?
a. 100–199
b. 900–999
c. 700–799

I Have Shaken Hands with a Great Many Friends

Chief Joseph

I have shaken hands with a great many friends,
But there are some things I want to know which
   no one seems to be able to explain . . .
I do not understand why nothing is done for my
   people.
I have heard talk and talk, but nothing is done.

Good words do not last long until they amount
   to something.
Words do not pay for my dead people.
They do not pay for my country, now overrun by
   white men.
They do not protect my father's grave.
They do not pay for my horses and cattle. . . .
Good words will not give my people health and
   stop them from dying.
Good words will not get my people a home where
   they can live in peace
   and take care of themselves.
I am tired of talk that comes to nothing.
It makes my heart sick when I remember
   all the good words and all the broken
   promises. . . .

If the white man wants to live in peace
   with the Indian, he can live in peace.
There need be no trouble.
Treat all men alike.
Give them all the same law.
Give them all an even chance to live and
   grow. . . .
The earth is the mother of all people,
And all people should have equal rights upon it.
You might as well expect the rivers to run
   backward
     as that any man who was born free
     should be contented penned up
     and denied liberty to go where he pleases. . . .

Let me be a free man—
Free to travel,
Free to stop,
Free to work,
Free to trade where I choose,
Free to choose my own teachers,
Free to follow the religion of my fathers,
Free to think and talk and act for myself—
And I will obey every law,
    or submit to the penalty.

About the Author

Chief Joseph (1841-1904)

Chief Joseph was a great leader of the Nez Percé Indians of Oregon. His Indian name, Hinmaton-Yalakitt, means "Thunder Traveling over the Mountains." In 1877, Chief Joseph led the Nez Percés through the Northwest on a march toward freedom. After many battles, eleven weeks, and 1700 miles, they were turned back by the United States Army, just 30 miles from Canada. Joseph's speeches and writings show the courage, dignity, and strength of character for which he was known. The selection included here is taken from an essay, "An Indian's View of Indian Affairs," which was published in the *North American Review*. Chief Joseph died on the Colville Reservation in Washington.

Focus on the Essay

An essay is a short composition on one subject. Essays are usually written in prose form and are considered nonfiction.

The **author's purpose** is the reason behind his or her writing. The author's purpose may be to entertain, to inform, to teach, or to convince the reader of a certain idea.

▶ **1.** In this essay, Chief Joseph's purpose was to _____.
a. amuse his readers
b. let his readers know about life on a reservation
c. explain his thoughts and feelings about the conditions of the American Indian

2. The selection ends with a plea for _____.
a. equality and freedom
b. payment for horses and cattle
c. a peace treaty

Focus on the Language

Metaphor

▶ **1.** Which line from Chief Joseph's essay is a metaphor?
a. The earth is the mother of all people.
b. Let me be a free man.
c. Give them all the same law.

Antonym

▶ **2.** An antonym for *protect* is _____.
a. *attack*
b. *defend*
c. *borrow*

Homonym

▶ **3.** A homonym for *peace* is _____.
a. *piece*
b. *war*
c. *friend*

43

Abraham Lincoln's Boyhood

Carl Sandburg

*He lived with trees, with the bush
wet with shining raindrops. He lived
with open sky and weather and the
ax. Those were his companions.*

When he was eleven years old, Abraham Lincoln's young body began to change. As the months and years went by, he noticed his lean wrists getting longer, his legs, too, and he was now looking over the heads of other boys. Men said, "Land o' Goshen, that boy air a-growin'!"

As he took on more length, they said he was shooting up into the air like green corn in the summer of a good corn year. So he grew. When he reached seventeen years of age, they measured him. He was nearly six feet, four inches high, from the bottom of his moccasins to the top of his skull.

These were years he was handling the ax. He was handling the ax nearly all the time. The insides of his hands were hard as leather. He cleared openings in the timber, cut logs, split firewood, built pigpens.

He learned how to measure with his eye the half-circle swing of the ax. He could cut as deep as possible into a tree trunk. The trick of swinging his body easily on the hips so as to throw the heaviest possible weight into the blow of the ax—he learned that.

On winter mornings, he wiped the frost from the ax handle, sniffed sparkles of air into his lungs, and beat blows steadily into a big tree—till it fell. He sat on the main log and ate his noon dinner of corn bread and fried salt pork.

He learned the secrets of black walnut and black oak, hickory and elm and dogwood. He could guess close to the time of the year, to the week of the month, by the way the leaves and branches of trees looked. He sniffed the seasons.

Often he worked alone in the timber, all day long with only the sound of his own ax, or his own voice speaking to himself, or the cracking and swaying of branches in the wind, and the cries of animals—the brown and silver-gray squirrels, the hawks, crows, turkeys, sparrows, and occasionally wildcats.

The tricks of the sky, how to read clear skies and cloudy weather, the creeping vines of ivy and wild grape, the ways of snow, rain, sleet—he tried to read their secrets. He tried to be friendly with their mystery.

So he grew to become hard, tough, wiry. One of his neighbors said he was strong as three men. Another said, "He can sink an ax deeper into wood than any man I ever saw." And another, "If you heard him fellin' trees in a clearin', you would say there was three men at work by the way the trees fell."

He was more than a tough, long, rawboned boy. He amazed men with his lifting power. He put his shoulders under a new-built corncrib one day and walked away with it to where the farmer wanted it. Four men, ready with poles to put under it and carry it, didn't need their poles. He played the same trick with a chicken house. They said that it weighed six hundred pounds.

So he grew, living in that cabin for a home. He slept in the loft, climbing up at night to a bed just under the roof. Sometimes the snow and the rain drove through the cracks. He ate sometimes at a table where the family had only one thing to eat—potatoes.

Abe knew the sleep that comes after long hours of work out of doors. He knew the feeling of simple food changing into blood and muscle. In those young years, he worked clearing timberland for pasture and corn crops. He cut loose the brush, piled it, and burned it. He split rails, drove the plow, planted, hoed, milked cows, churned butter, helped neighbors.

He found he was fast and strong when he went against other boys in sports. On farms where he worked, he held his own at wrestling. The time came when around Gentryville and Spencer County he was known as the best "rassler" of all, the champion. In jumping, foot racing, pitching the crowbar, he won against the lads of his age always. And he usually won against those older than himself.

He earned his board, clothes, and lodgings sometimes working for a neighbor farmer. He watched his father, while helping make cabinets, coffins, cupboards, window frames, doors. Hammers and saws he understood.

When he was eighteen years old, he could take an ax at the end of the handle and hold it out in a straight line, easy and steady. He had strong shoulder muscles and steady wrists early in life. He walked thirty-four miles in one day, just on an errand, to please himself, to hear a lawyer make a speech. He could tell his body to do almost impossible things, and the body obeyed.

Growing from boy to man, he was alone a good deal of the time. Days came often when he was by himself all the time except at breakfast and supper hours in the cabin home. In some years, more of his time was spent in loneliness than in the company of other people. It happened, too, that this loneliness he knew was not like that of people in cities who can look from a window on streets where people pass. It was the loneliness of the wilderness he knew.

He lived with trees, with the bush wet with shining raindrops. He lived with the burning leaves of autumn, with a lone wild duck riding a north wind. He lived with open sky and weather and the ax. Those were his companions.

His moccasined feet in the wintertime knew the white of snowdrifts piled against timber slopes or across the fields. In the summertime, his bare feet grew tough in the gravel of green streams.

He found in his life there were chances for growth. And so he grew.

About the Author

Carl Sandburg (1878-1967) _____

Carl Sandburg was one of America's finest poets and biographers. His six-volume biography of Abraham Lincoln took nearly twenty years to write. Many consider it one of the greatest biographies ever written.

Sandburg's poetry is powerful and realistic and deals with the hopes and fears of the common people. In 1940, Sandburg won the Pulitzer prize for history. He received the Pulitzer prize for poetry in 1951. "Abraham Lincoln's Boyhood" is from *Abraham Lincoln: The Prairie Years*.

Focus on the Biography

A biography is a type of literature in which a writer tells about someone else's life. A biography is classified as non-fiction.

Main Character

▶ **1.** The main character in this biography is _____ .
  a. Carl Sandburg
  b. the narrator
  c. Abraham Lincoln

Author's Purpose

▶ **2.** What was Carl Sandburg's reason for writing this biography?
  a. to convince his readers that it's important to know how to handle an ax
  b. to entertain his readers with a story about an imaginary character
  c. to inform his readers about Abraham Lincoln's life

Setting

▶ **3.** The setting of this biography is a _____ .
  a. wilderness area
  b. large town
  c. riverboat

4. The time at which this story takes place is _____ .
  a. the 1700s
  b. the 1800s
  c. the 1900s

Point of View

▶ **5.** From which point of view is this biography told?
  a. the first-person point of view
  b. the third-person point of view
  c. Abraham Lincoln's point of view

Focus on the Language

Dialect is the local use of language. In different parts of the country, words or phrases can be spoken in different ways.

▶ **1.** Which sentence from "Abraham Lincoln's Boyhood" contains an example of dialect?
a. Men said, "Land o' Goshen, that boy air a-growin'!"
b. He grew to be hard, tough, wiry.
c. One said, "He can swing an ax better than any man I ever saw."

Simile

▶ **2.** Following are three descriptions of Abraham Lincoln. Which one contains a simile?
a. He had strong shoulder muscles and steady wrists.
b. He was nearly six feet, four inches high.
c. His hands were hard as leather.

Find Out More

An **encyclopedia** is a set of books that gives information about many subjects. The books are arranged alphabetically by subject.

▶ **1.** This biography tells about Abraham Lincoln's boyhood. To find out about Lincoln's later life, in which volume of the encyclopedia should you look?
a. 1   b. 5   c. 7

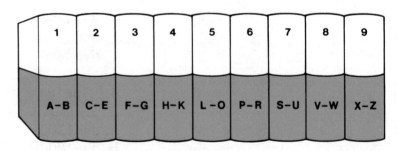

2. In what year was Abraham Lincoln first elected President? To find the answer, look in the encyclopedia.
a. 1860   b. 1864   c. 1865

48

I Have a Dream

Martin Luther King, Jr.

I say to you today, my friends,
   even though we face the difficulties
   of today and tomorrow, I still have a dream.

It is a dream deeply rooted in the American dream.

I have a dream that one day this nation will rise up
   and live out the true meaning of its creed:
   "We hold these truths to be self-evident,
   that all men are created equal." . . .

I have a dream that my four little children
   will one day live in a nation where
   they will not be judged by the color of their skin,
   but by the content of their character.

I have a dream today! . . .

I have a dream that one day
   "Every valley shall be exalted
   and every hill and mountain shall be made low.

   The rough places will be made plain
   and the crooked places will be made straight
   and the glory of the Lord shall be revealed,
   and all flesh shall see it together."

This is our hope.

This is the faith that I go back to the South with. . . .

With this faith, we shall be able to transform
the jangling discords of our nation
into a beautiful symphony of brotherhood.

With this faith
we will be able to work together,
to pray together,
to struggle together,
to go to jail together,
to stand up for freedom together
knowing that we will be free one day.

And this will be the day.
This will be the day
when all of God's children
will be able to sing with new meaning:
"My country 'tis of thee
sweet land of liberty
of thee I sing.
Land where my fathers died
land of the pilgrim's pride
from every mountain side, let freedom ring."

And if America is to be a great nation,
this must become true.

So let freedom ring
from the . . . hilltops of New Hampshire;
let freedom ring
from the mighty mountains of New York;
let freedom ring
from the heightening Alleghanies of Pennsylvania;
let freedom ring
from the snow capped Rockies of Colorado;
let freedom ring
from the . . . slopes of California.

51

But not only that.

Let freedom ring
   from Stone Mountain of Georgia;
   let freedom ring
   from Lookout Mountain of Tennessee;
   let freedom ring
   from every hill and molehill of Mississippi.

From every mountainside, let freedom ring.

And when this happens
   and when we allow freedom to ring,
   when we let it ring from every village
   and every hamlet,
   from every state and every city,
   we will be able to speed up that day
   when all God's children,
   black men and white men,
   Jews and Gentiles,
   Protestants and Catholics,
   will be able to join hands and sing
   in the words of the old Negro spiritual:

"Free at last. Free at last.

Thank God Almighty,

We are free at last."

About the Author

Martin Luther King, Jr. (1929-1968) ____

Martin Luther King, Jr., was born in Atlanta, Georgia, the son of a preacher. During the 1950s and 1960s, Reverend King was one of the nation's strongest leaders in the Civil Rights movement. He was a powerful speaker, whose words had the ability to stir his audience. The above is taken from a speech delivered before a huge gathering in Washington in August, 1963. Martin Luther King, Jr., received the Nobel peace prize in 1964. In 1968, King was assassinated in Memphis, Tennessee.

Focus on the Speech

Author's Viewpoint

► **1.** Martin Luther King, Jr., believed that _____.
a. dreaming is not worthwhile
b. for America to be a great nation, everyone must be free
c. there are no real problems in America

The way a writer uses language is called the **author's style.** The style includes the author's choice of words and the arrangement of words and sentences.

► **2.** Part of the power of this selection lies in the repetition of phrases. Which phrase is repeated?
a. "I have a dream."
b. "Let freedom ring."
c. both of the above

An **allusion** is a reference to some person, place, thing, or event that a reader is likely to recognize. For example, in this speech, King makes an allusion to the Declaration of Independence when he quotes the lines, "We hold these truths to be self-evident, that all men are created equal."

► **3.** In his speech, King alluded to the Old Testament. Which line begins a biblical quote?
a. "I still have a dream . . ."
b. "Every valley shall be exalted . . ."
c. "My country 'tis of thee . . ."

Focus on the Language

Figurative Language

► **1.** "We shall be able to transform the jangling discords of our nation into a beautiful symphony of brotherhood." This means that _____.
a. a divided country will be brought together
b. music has the power to calm everyone's nerves
c. no one can tell what the future will be

Word in Context

► **2.** What is the meaning of the word *plain* in the following sentence?
The rough places will be made plain.
a. smooth
b. open
c. simple

Lineage

Margaret Walker

My grandmothers were strong.
They followed plows and bent to toil.
They moved through fields sowing seed.
They touched earth and grain grew.
They were full of sturdiness and singing.
My grandmothers were strong.

My grandmothers are full of memories
Smelling of soap and onions and wet clay
With veins rolling roughly over quick hands
They have many clean words to say.
My grandmothers were strong.
Why am I not as they?

Focus on the Poem

The **title** or name of a poem can help you know what the poem is about. This poem is called "Lineage." The word means "the line from which a family has descended." Your lineage includes your parents, grandparents, etc.

A **stanza** of a poem or song is a group of lines that goes together. For example, "Lineage" is made up of two stanzas. Each stanza is six lines long.

Imagery

Author's Viewpoint

Synonym

▶ **1.** Based on the title of this poem, you can guess that the poem is about _____.
a. the poet's family background
b. the poet's hopes for the future
c. the poet's job

▶ **2.** Which of the following statements is true about the first stanza of this poem?
a. The four middle lines begin with the word "they."
b. The first and last lines are the same.
c. both of the above

▶ **3.** In each stanza, the poet recalls her grandmothers. What picture does she create of them?
a. She shows them to be hard workers.
b. She shows that they were weak.
c. She pictures them as old and tired.

▶ **4.** How does the author compare herself to her grandmothers?
a. She thinks she is stronger than they were.
b. She thinks she is just like them.
c. She thinks her grandmothers were stronger than she is.

▶ **5.** A synonym for *sowing* is _____.
a. *sewing*
b. *planting*
c. *touching*

Unit Review

Write your answers on a separate sheet of paper.

1. The way an author feels about his or her subject matter is known as the author's _____.
   a. style
   b. viewpoint
   c. purpose

2. Write *true* or *false* next to each of the following statements.
   a. Stories about real people and events are considered nonfiction. _____
   b. Fiction is about imaginary people and events. _____
   c. Autobiographies are classified as fiction. _____

3. The narrator of the biography, "Abraham Lincoln's Boyhood," is _____.
   a. Abraham Lincoln
   b. Mark Twain
   c. Carl Sandburg

4. Which work is told from the first-person point of view?
   a. "I Have a Dream"
   b. *Life on the Mississippi*
   c. both of the above

5. Match each word with its definition.
   a. biography — a short, nonfiction composition on one subject __
   b. autobiography — a type of literature in which a person tells about his or her life __
   c. essay — a type of literature in which a writer tells about someone else's life __

Reviewing the Language

1. Which sentence from "Abraham Lincoln's Boyhood" contains an example of dialect?

   a. Abe knew the sleep that comes after long hours of work out of doors.
   b. He found in his life there were chances for growth.
   c. He was known as the best "rassler" of all, the champion.

2. Following are three sentences from *Life on the Mississippi*. Which one contains alliteration?

   a. Mr. Bixby headed toward the shore.
   b. He was steering it straight at a star.
   c. In a few moments, the boat's nose came to the land.

3. Which of the following sentences contains a cliché?

   a. I dream that my children will not be judged by the color of their skin, but by the content of their character.
   b. His moccasined feet knew the white of snowdrifts piled against timber slopes.
   c. It was like waving a red flag at a bull.

4. What is the meaning of the word *check* in the following sentence?
   I kept my feelings in check and went about my job.

   a. money
   b. control
   c. to examine or correct

Talking It Over

1. In this unit, various writers offer "Reflections of America." What did the reflections of Louisa May Alcott, Martin Luther King, Jr., and Chief Joseph have in common? In what ways were they different? How were these people alike? What do their reflections tell us about the kind of people they were?

2. Who do you think had a more interesting childhood, Mark Twain or Abraham Lincoln? How did their childhood experiences help make them the men they later became?

3. In "Lineage," Margaret Walker remembers her grandmothers. How did she picture them? Why might the poet believe that she is not as strong as they were? In what ways might the poet be stronger than she realizes?

57

unit 3

Double-Edged Dreams

If a man could have half his wishes, he would double his troubles.

—Benjamin Franklin

The Monkey's Paw

W. W. Jacobs

*Fate ruled people's lives. Those who
fooled with it did so to their sorrow.*

Part I

Outside, the night was cold and
wet. But in the house, the blinds were
down and the fire in the fireplace
burned brightly.

Mr. White and his son were playing
chess.

"Listen to the wind, Herbert," said
the father, looking up, hoping that
the boy wouldn't see the bad move he
had just made.

"I'm listening," said his son, staring at the board. He moved a piece.
"Check."

"I don't think Sergeant Morris will
come tonight," said the father.

The boy smiled and made the final
move. "Checkmate!" he said.

"That's the trouble living out here!"
cried the father loudly. "Of all the out-
of-the-way places to live in, this is the
worst!"

"Now, now, dear," said his wife,
knitting near the fire. "Never mind.
Perhaps you'll win the next game."

Just then, they heard the gate
banging loudly, and the sound of
heavy footsteps coming toward the
door.

"Here he is," said Herbert.

The old man rose and opened the
door. There stood a tall, powerful man
with sharp eyes and rough skin.

"Come in," said the old man to the
new arrival. He turned to his family.
"This is my friend, Sergeant Morris."

The sergeant shook hands and took
the seat by the fire. Mr. White got out
whiskey and glasses. He put a kettle
on the fire.

After the third glass, the sergeant's
eyes grew brighter. He began to talk
easily. The little family circle listened
with interest to everything he said. He
had been to many far-off lands. He

spoke of strange scenes, brave deeds, war, hunger, and unusual peoples.

"I'd like to go to India myself," said the old man. "Just to look around a bit, you know."

"Better stay where you are," said the sergeant, shaking his head. He put down the empty glass and, sighing softly, shook his head.

"I should like to see those old temples and magicians," said the old man. "What was that you started telling me the other day—about a monkey's paw or something?"

"Nothing," said the other hastily. "At least nothing worth hearing."

"Monkey's paw?" said Mrs. White curiously.

"Well, it's just a bit of what you might call magic, perhaps," said the sergeant.

His three listeners leaned forward eagerly.

The sergeant put a hand into his pocket. "It's just an ordinary little paw," he said, "dried up like a mummy."

He took something out of his pocket and held it out. Mrs. White drew back with a look of shock on her face. But her son took the paw and examined it closely.

"And what is there special about it?" asked Mr. White as he took it from his son and placed it on the table.

"It had a spell put on it by an old man of India," said the sergeant. "He was a very holy man. He wanted to show that fate ruled people's lives and that those who fooled with it did so to their sorrow. He put a spell on it so that three men could each have three wishes from it."

The sergeant spoke very seriously. But the three listeners laughed.

"Well, why don't *you* make three wishes, sir?" asked Herbert White, smiling.

The sergeant's face turned pale as he stared at the boy. "I have," he said softly.

"And were the three wishes granted?" asked Mrs. White.

"They were," said the sergeant, shuddering slightly.

"And has anybody else wished?" asked the old lady.

"The first man had his three wishes, yes. I don't know what the first two were." Here the sergeant stopped. "But the third wish was for death! That's how I got the paw."

His voice was so grave that the group fell silent. At last, the old man said, "If you've had your three wishes, the monkey's paw is no good to you now. Why do you keep it?"

The sergeant shook his head. "I did have some idea of selling it," he said. "But I don't think I will. It has caused enough trouble already. Besides, people won't buy it. Some think it's a fairy tale. And others want to try it first and pay me later."

"If you could have another three wishes," said the old man, looking at him closely, "would you have them?"

"I don't know," said the sergeant. "I don't know."

The sergeant looked closely at the paw. Suddenly, he threw it upon the fire. Mr. White, with a slight cry, bent down and pulled it out.

"Better let it burn," said the soldier seriously.

"If you don't want it," said the old man, "give it to me."

"I won't!" said his friend. "I threw it in the fire. If you keep it, don't blame me for what happens! Throw it on the fire again, I tell you!"

But the other just shook his head and looked at the paw.

"How do you do it?" the old man asked.

"Hold it up in your right hand and wish aloud," said the sergeant. "But I'm warning you."

"It *does* sound like a fairy tale," said Mrs. White. She rose and began to set the table. "Don't you think you might wish for four pairs of hands for me. I'd finish my work in half the time."

There was a look of alarm in the sergeant's face. "If you must wish," he said sharply, "be careful what you ask!"

After their guest had left, Mrs. White turned toward her husband. "Did you give him anything for the paw?" she asked.

"Just a little something," he said, turning slightly red. "He didn't want it. But I made him take it. And he begged me again to throw the paw away."

"Why, father," said Herbert, with a twinkle in his eyes. "We're going to be rich and famous and happy. Wish to be a king. That's a good start!"

Mr. White took the paw from his pocket and looked at it. "I don't know what to wish for, and that's a fact," he said slowly. "It seems to me I've got all I want."

"You'd be happy to pay off the house, wouldn't you?" said Herbert. He put his hand on his father's shoulder. "Well wish for five hundred dollars, then. That'll just do it."

The father smiled, feeling a little ashamed. He held up the paw. His son, with a wink at Mrs. White, sat down at the piano and struck a few notes.

"I wish for five hundred dollars!" the old man said clearly.

A loud crash from the piano greeted these words. At that instant, the old man gave a loud cry. His wife and son ran toward him.

"It moved!" he cried. He looked at the paw as it lay on the floor. "As I made my wish, the paw twisted in my hands like a snake!"

"Well I don't see the money," said the son. He picked up the paw and placed it on the table. "And I bet I never will."

"It must have been your imagination," said Mrs. White to her husband.

He shook his head. "No, it moved," he said. "Never mind, though. There's no harm done. But it gave me a shock just the same."

They sat down by the fire again. Outside, the wind howled worse than ever. The old man jumped at the sound of a door which banged upstairs. A fearful silence settled upon all three. At last, the old couple rose to go to bed.

"Look for the cash in a big bag in the middle of your bed," said Herbert, smiling. Then he wished them good night.

Part II

A bright winter's sun shone on the breakfast table the next morning. The family laughed about what had happened the night before.

"I suppose all old soldiers are the same," said Mrs. White. "The idea of our listening to such nonsense! How could wishes be granted? And if they could, how could five hundred dollars hurt you, father?"

"Might drop on his head from the sky," said Herbert, joking.

"The sergeant said bad luck always follows," said the old man. "He said it happens every time."

"Well, don't spend the money before I come home from work," said Herbert as he rose from the table.

His mother laughed and followed him to the door. She watched him go down the road before she returned to the breakfast table.

The day seemed to go more slowly than usual. Mr. White and his wife were rather nervous. As they sat down to dinner, Mrs. White said, "Herbert will have some more of his funny remarks, I expect, when he comes home."

"Probably," said Mr. White. "Still, the thing moved in my hands. I'm sure of it."

"You *thought* it did," said the old lady softly.

"I say it *did*! There was no *thought* about it. It's just that I had—what's the matter?"

His wife did not answer. She was watching a man outside. He appeared to be trying to make up his mind about whether to enter. She thought about the five hundred dollars, for she noticed that the stranger was very well dressed. Three times, he stopped at the gate and then left. The fourth time, he threw it open and walked up the path. Mrs. White went to the door and invited him in.

For several minutes, he was strangely silent.

"I—was asked to call," he said at last. "I come from the office of Meggins and Meggins where your son—"

The old lady jumped. "Is anything the matter?" she asked breathlessly. "Has anything happened to Herbert? What is it? What is it?"

"There, there, mother," said Mr. White, hastily. "Sit down and don't jump to conclusions." He turned to the stranger. "You've not brought bad news, I'm sure, sir," he said.

"I'm sorry—" began the stranger.

"Is he hurt?" demanded the mother.

The visitor shook his head yes. "Badly hurt," he said softly. "But he is not in any pain."

"Oh thank goodness," said the woman. "Thank goodness for that. Thank—"

She stopped suddenly as the true meaning of the words came to her. She looked at the stranger, but he turned his face away. The old lady caught her breath. She turned to her husband and put her hand on his. There was a long silence.

"He was crushed in the machinery," said the visitor at last, in a low voice.

"Crushed in the machinery," repeated Mr. White, looking dazed.

"Yes. He is dead."

Mr. White stared out of the window. "He was our only son," he said finally to the visitor. "It is hard."

The visitor coughed. He walked slowly to the window. "The company wanted me to say how sorry they are for your great loss," he said without turning around. "Meggins and Meggins takes no blame for the accident. But because of your son's services, they wish to give you a certain sum of money."

Mr. White dropped his wife's hand. He gazed with a look of horror at his visitor. "How much?" he asked.

"Five hundred dollars."

The old man did not hear his wife's screams. He threw out his hands like a blind man and fell to the floor.

Part III

Two miles away, in the new cemetery, Herbert was buried. It was all over so quickly, the old couple could hardly believe it had happened. The days passed slowly. Sometimes, they hardly spoke a word for now they had nothing to talk about. Their days were long and weary.

About a week later, the old man suddenly awoke in the middle of the night. He stretched out his hand and found himself alone. He heard his wife weeping near the window.

He raised himself in bed. "Come back," he called to her, tenderly. "You will be cold."

"It is colder for my son," she answered and began to cry again.

His eyes were heavy with sleep. The sound of her sobs died on his ears. He began to doze off when a sudden cry from his wife awoke him.

"The monkey's paw!" she cried wildly. "The monkey's paw!"

He jumped up in alarm. "Where? Where is it? What's the matter?"

She came running across the room toward him. "I want it," she said quietly. "You haven't destroyed it?"

"It's on the shelf in the parlor," he answered. "Why?"

She bent over and kissed him on the cheek. "I only just thought of it," she said wildly. "Why didn't I think of it before? Why didn't you think of it?"

"Think of what?" he asked.

"The other two wishes," she answered quickly. "We've only had one."

"Wasn't that enough?" he demanded angrily.

"No," she cried loudly. "We'll have one more. Go down and get it quickly and wish that our boy were alive again!"

The man sat up in bed. "You are mad!" he cried, shocked.

"Get it," she repeated. "Get it quickly and wish. Oh, my boy! My boy!"

Her husband struck a match and lit the candle. "Get back to bed," he said. "You don't know what you're saying!"

"We had the first wish granted," she said wildly. "Why not the second?"

But the old man did not move.

"Go get it and wish!" cried the old woman. She dragged him toward the door.

He went down in the darkness and made his way to the parlor. There on the shelf was the monkey's paw. Suddenly, he was filled with a horrible fear—that the wish might bring him his son, broken and crushed, before he had time to get out of the room. He caught his breath. For a moment, he could not find the door. His body grew cold. He felt his way around the table and finally headed back to his wife.

Her face seemed changed as he entered the room. It was pale and seemed to have a strange look to it. He was afraid of her.

"Wish!" she cried, in a strong voice.

"It is foolish and wicked," he said.

"Wish!" she repeated.

He raised his hand. "I wish my son alive again."

The paw fell to the floor, and he looked at it with terror. Then he sank, shaking, into a chair. With burning eyes, the old woman walked to the window and raised the blinds.

He sat until he was chilled with cold. He looked now and then at the old woman staring out of the window. After a while, the candle burned out, leaving the room in darkness. Finally, the old man crept back to bed. He was greatly relieved that the paw had failed. Soon he heard his wife coming to bed.

Neither spoke. In the silence, they could hear the ticking of a clock. The darkness pressed upon them. Finally, the husband took the box of matches and struck one. He went downstairs for a candle.

At the foot of the stairs, the match went out. He stopped to strike another. At the same moment, a soft knock sounded on the front door.

The matches fell from his hand. He stood without moving. He held his breath until the knock was repeated. Then he turned and rushed swiftly back to his room. He closed the door behind him. A third knock sounded through the house.

"What's that?" cried the old woman, jumping up.

"A rat," said the old man shaking, "a rat. It passed me on the stairs."

His wife sat up in bed listening. A loud knock sounded through the house.

"It's Herbert!" she screamed. "It's Herbert!"

She ran to the bedroom door. But her husband was before her. He caught her by the arm and held tightly.

"What are you going to do?" he whispered hoarsely.

"It's my boy! It's Herbert!" she cried. "What are you holding me for? Let me go. I must open the front door."

"Don't let *it* in!" cried the old man, shaking.

"Are you afraid of your own son?" she cried. "Let me go! I'm coming, Herbert! I'm coming!"

There was another knock, and another. The old woman pulled free and ran from the room. Her husband called after her as she hurried downstairs. He heard the chain rattle and the lower door bolt open. Then he heard the old woman's voice.

"The upper bolt," she cried loudly. "Help me. I can't reach it!"

But her husband was on his hands and knees. He was wildly searching for the paw. *If only he could find it before the thing got in!*

Knock after knock sounded through the house. He could hear his wife dragging a chair to the door. He heard the creaking of the bolt as she fought to release it. At that very moment, he found the monkey's paw. Wildly, he made his third and last wish!

The knocking suddenly stopped. He heard the chair being pulled away. He heard the door being opened. A cold wind blew up the staircase. A loud cry of disappointment from his wife gave him courage. He rushed down the stairs and out to the gate. The street lamp shone on an empty road.

About the Author

W. W. Jacobs (1863-1943) _____

William Wymark Jacobs, best known as W. W. Jacobs, was born in London and was educated in private schools. At the age of twenty, he began writing humorous articles in order to make extra money. When his first book, *Many Cargoes*, was published in 1896, he gave up his job with the civil service to devote himself full time to writing.

Jacobs's short stories are known for their sly humor, interesting characterizations, and unusual plots. Jacobs's most famous story is the chilling classic, "The Monkey's Paw."

Focus on the Story

Setting

▶ **1.** Which of the following best describes the setting of the "The Monkey's Paw"?
a. a large, crowded city
b. a house in an out-of-the-way place
c. a temple in India

The setting can create an **atmosphere.** The atmosphere helps the reader feel the same way that the characters feel.

▶ **2.** Which word best describes the atmosphere of "The Monkey's Paw"?
a. calm
b. joyous
c. frightening

Many stories contain a **conflict** between characters. A conflict is a fight or a difference of opinion.

▶ **3.** At the end of "The Monkey's Paw," the conflict is between _____ .
a. Mr. White and Sergeant Morris
b. Mrs. White and Herbert
c. Mr. and Mrs. White

The **theme** of the story is the main idea. The details in a story help develop the theme.

▶ **4.** What is the theme of this story?
a. It is silly to believe in magic.
b. It can be dangerous to fool with fate.
c. One should never accept a gift from a friend.

Narrator

▶ **5.** The narrator of "The Monkey's Paw" is _____ .
a. Mr. White
b. Herbert
c. not a character in the story

68

Focus on the Language

Concrete words name things that can be touched, heard, smelled, seen, or tasted.

Examples:
- boat
- magazine
- bread

Abstract words name ideas that *cannot* be touched, heard, smelled, seen, or tasted.

Examples:
- courage
- joy
- friendship

Word in Context

▶ **1.** Which of the following is a group of concrete words?
a. fireplace, gate, machinery
b. magic, imagination, shining
c. horrible, serious, twisted

▶ **2.** To describe the characters' feelings in the story, the author used abstract words. Which group below contains abstract words?
a. cemetery, door, piano
b. chair, knees, clock
c. horror, shame, fear

▶ **3.** What is the meaning of the word *spell* in the sentence below?
It had a spell put on it by an old man of India.
a. letters in a word
b. period of time
c. magic charm

Talk It Over

1. Could Herbert's death have been a "coincidence"? If so, can you make up a reasonable explanation for the ending of the story?
2. What was Mr. White's last wish? Why did he make it?
3. Do people today usually believe in "good luck charms"?
4. If you had three wishes, what would they be?

The Pardoner's Tale

Geoffrey Chaucer

Is it so dangerous this Death to meet?
I will seek him with my friends on
every street.

In Flanders once, there lived a gang who loved to sing and dance, to eat and drink with all their might, to play at dice both day and night. And so they did the Devil's business.

Three of these, of whom I speak, sat down at a tavern on a crowded street. And they saw a body carried out.

"Who is that man?" asked one.

"A friend of yours," the answer came. "He suddenly was killed tonight. There came a sly thief that men call Death. You may have heard, he quickly kills without a word. A thousand he has murdered here."

" 'Tis true," the owner of the tavern said. "In a village just a mile away, women, men, and children lay. He killed them all. And that is where he lives, I hear. You would be wise to not go near."

The first man said:

"Is it so dangerous this Death to meet? I will seek him with my friends on every street. We three like brothers will be. So let us each shake hands and vow this fellow, Death, to kill."

So saying this, the three drank many another cup. And at last, one spoke up. "Death shall be dead," he said, "if we can but catch him."

Towards the village they then set out. When they had less than half a mile gone, they saw an old man sitting on a stone. He was wrapped in robes; his face was filled with wrinkles and lines.

"Old man," said the boldest of the three. "Why are you covered up except for your face? And how have you lived to such an old age?"

"No one," he said, "will trade his youth for my ripe old age. Even Death will not take my life. All day long, I knock with my stick on the ground and say, 'Mother Earth, let me in. I am hardly more than bones and skin. Let this weary body rest. Give me a grave to place my chest.' But that favor to me she will not give. And so it is Death lets me live."

With that, the old man rose to go.

"Not so fast," said one of the three. "You shall not leave so easily. You spoke just now of that traitor, Death, who takes away both life and breath. Without question, you are his spy. Tell us where he is, or you shall die!"

"Now, sirs," said he, "if you are so eager to find Death, turn up this crooked path. For I left him back there under a tree. But whatever threats you may have made, I think you will find him unafraid."

Each of the three ran until he came to the tree. And there they found gold coins, bright and round. Seven bags of them lay on the ground.

When they these riches saw, they decided to look for Death no more.

The worst of them spoke first:

"Brothers," he said, "listen to what I say. For my mind is sharp, though I often joke and play. Fortune has given us this treasure, so that we may fill our lives with pleasure. We must carry this gold away, for surely here it cannot stay. But truly by day it may not be done. Men would say we were thieves. They'd hang us every one. The treasure must be carried off by night. That is the way to do it right."

"Let us all draw straws. Whoever draws the shortest one into town shall quickly run. He shall bring us back both bread and wine. The other two shall guard the treasure well. When it is night, we shall decide the safest place to bring the gold to hide."

The shortest fell to the youngest of the three. He set out for town immediately. As soon as he was gone, one said to the other, "You know I gave you my hand as a brother. Listen well to what I say. Here is plenty of gold as you can see, to be divided among us three. If I can fix it, as I could, so that the two of us share it, wouldn't that be good?"

The other answered, "That would be good, I do agree. But I don't know how that might be. He knows full well the gold is with us two. What shall we say? What shall we do?"

"Now," said the first, "you know that one man is weaker than two.

When our friend returns, let him speak to you. And while his back is turned, I'll run him through."

"Then when he's down," the second man said, "I'll use *my* knife. And so between us, we'll end his life. And after we have made this kill, we can play at dice all day at will."

And so the two men gave each other their word that later that day they would kill the third.

The youngest, who went into town, could not forget the sight of what they'd found. "Oh," he said, "if I could have that treasure all to myself, there would be no one under the sky who should live as merry a life as I."

At last he knew just what to do. He would buy some poison and kill the other two. And once he had this idea, he went into town to a druggist near. He asked for poison to kill his rats.

The druggist said, "A powerful poison I shall give. No creature in the world can taste it and live."

After taking the poison, he bought three bottles of wine. Into two of them he poured his poison. But he kept his own pure and fine. He planned to work all night, alone, carrying the gold back to his home. Then he returned to his friends.

What more is there to say? For just as the two had planned, they killed the third. And when this was done, one of them said, "Now let us drink and be merry. And afterwards, we will his body bury."

And by chance, he took one of the bottles with the poison there. He drank and gave his friend the bottle to share. Having tasted the poison which was inside, within a few minutes both men died.

And so there they lay dead on the ground, all three, next to the bags of gold by the tree.

About the Author

Geoffrey Chaucer (1340-1400) ———

Geoffrey Chaucer is usually thought of as the first great English poet and is often called the father of English poetry. He is best known for *The Canterbury Tales,* a group of stories told by pilgrims on their way to the city of Canterbury. According to Chaucer's plan, each pilgrim would tell two stories on the way to Canterbury and two on the way home. Of the 120 tales planned, only 22 were completed. "The Pardoner's Tale" is one of these.

Chaucer died in 1400 and was buried in Westminster Abbey in London, in what has come to be called "The Poet's Corner." This section of the Abbey is reserved as the burial place for the very greatest of English poets.

Focus on the Story

The **time span** of a story is the time between the beginning and the ending of the story.

▶ 1. What is the time span of this story?
a. about a day
b. a week or two
c. a minute

Motive

▶ 2. Why were the three men looking for Death?
a. to ask for mercy
b. to complain about their friend who had died
c. to kill him

A story may contain a **moral**. The moral of a story is the lesson that it teaches.

▶ 3. Which sentence best states the moral of this story?
a. Those who place greed above friendship pay for it.
b. You should always trust your friends.
c. Great riches bring happiness.

Focus on the Language

Rhyme is the repetition of similar sounds.

Example:
• *Might* rhymes with *night*.
• *Heard* rhymes with *word*.

▶ 1. Which sentence from "The Pardoner's Tale" contains rhyme?
a. In a village just a mile away, women, men, and children lay.
b. Is it so dangerous this Death to meet?
c. So saying this, the three drank many another cup.

Rhythm is the regular rise and fall of sounds.

▶ 2. Which of the following is true about the story?
a. The rhythm is not really noticeable.
b. It is easy to hear the rise and fall of the rhythm.
c. The rhythm is the same as regular speech.

When vowel sounds are repeated within a sentence or a line of poetry, this is known as **assonance.**

Examples:
- h*i*de and w*i*se
- gl*o*w and sp*o*ke

Notice that while the vowel sounds are the same, the consonant sounds are different.

Slant rhymes are rhymes that are not true rhymes, but are used to create an effect.

Examples:
- *swim* and *time*
- *done* and *soon*

Personification

Talk It Over

▶ **3.** In the sentence below, which words illustrate assonance?
They played at dice both day and night.
a. *played* and *both*
b. *day* and *night*
c. *dice* and *night*

▶ **4.** Which sentence contains slant rhyme?
a. Here is gold as you can see to be divided among us three.
b. When they had less than half a mile gone, they saw an old man sitting on a stone.
c. Fortune has given us this treasure, so that we may fill our lives with pleasure.

▶ **5.** Which sentence does *not* contain personification?
a. Death spoke to me.
b. The old man rose to go.
c. Mother Earth refused my plea.

Below are expressions you probably have heard before. Explain how each one relates to "The Pardoner's Tale."

- All that glitters is not gold.
- A fool and his money are soon parted.
- There is no honor among thieves.
- Money is the root of all evil.
- With friends like that, who needs enemies?

The Rocking-Horse Winner

D. H. Lawrence

He would often sit on his big rocking-horse, charging madly into space, riding toward luck.

There was a woman who was beautiful. She started with all the advantages. Yet she had no luck. She married for love and the love turned to dust. She had good children. Yet she felt they had been thrust upon her. She could not love them. They looked at her coldly, as if they were finding fault with her. She always felt she must cover up some fault in herself. Yet what it was that she must cover up, she never knew. Even so, when her children were present, she always felt the center of her heart go hard. This troubled her. So, she was all the more gentle with her children, as if she loved them very much. Only she herself knew that the center of her heart was hard. She could not feel love. No, not for anybody. Everybody else said of her, "She is such a good mother. She loves her children." Only she and her children knew it was not so. They read it in each other's eyes.

There was a boy and two little girls. They lived in a pleasant house. They felt as though they were better than anyone in the neighborhood.

Although they lived in style, they always felt a tension in the house. There was never enough money. The mother had a small income, and the father had a small income. But they had not nearly enough for the social standing which they had to keep up. The father went into town to some office. But though he had good hopes, these hopes never turned into anything. There was always the feeling of a shortage of money.

At last, the mother said, "I will see if I can't make something!" But she did not know where to begin. She racked her brains. She tried this thing and the other. But she could not find anything successful. The failure made deep lines come into her face. Her children were growing up. They would have to go to school. There must be more money. The father seemed as if he never would be able to do anything worth doing. And the mother did not succeed any better.

And so the house came to be haunted by the unspoken words: *There must be more money! There must be more money!* The children could hear it all the time. But nobody said it aloud. They heard it at Christmas, when the expensive toys filled the nursery. Behind the shining new rocking-horse, behind the smart doll's-house, a voice would start whispering: "There *must* be more money! There *must* be more money!" And the children would stop playing to listen for a moment. They would look into each other's eyes to see if they had all heard. And each one saw in the eyes of the others that they too had heard. "There *must* be more money! There *must* be more money!"

It came whispering from the springs of the rocking-horse. Even the horse, bending its wooden head, heard it. The big doll, sitting so pink, could hear it quite plainly. The foolish puppy, too, heard the secret whisper all over the house: *"There must be more money!"*

"Mother," said the boy Paul one day, "why don't we keep a car of our own? Why do we always use uncle's or else a taxi?"

"Because we're the poor members of the family," said the mother.

"But why are we, mother?"

"Well, I suppose," she said slowly, "it's because your father has no luck."

The boy was silent for some time.

"Is luck money, mother?" he asked.

"No, Paul. Not quite. It's what causes you to have money."

"Oh," said the boy. "Then what is luck, mother?"

"It's what causes you to have money. If you're lucky you have money. That's why it's better to be born lucky than rich. If you're rich, you may lose your money. But if you're lucky, you will always get more money."

"Oh. Will you? And father is not lucky?"

"Very unlucky, I should say," she answered.

The boy watched her with unsure eyes.

"Why?" he asked.

"I don't know. Nobody ever knows why one person is lucky and another unlucky."

"Don't they? Nobody at all? Does *nobody* know?"

"Perhaps God. But He never tells."

"He ought to, then. And aren't you lucky either, mother?"

"I can't be. I married an unlucky husband."

"But by yourself, aren't you?"

"I used to think I was, before I married. Now I think I am very unlucky indeed."

"Why?"

"Well—never mind. Perhaps I'm not really," she said. The child looked at her to see if she meant it. But he saw by the lines of her mouth that she was only trying to hide something from him.

"Well, anyhow," he said, "I'm a lucky person!"

"Excellent!" said the mother, using one of her husband's words.

The boy saw she did not believe him. This angered him somewhat. It made him want to get her attention.

He went off by himself, looking for the clue to "luck." He wanted luck. He wanted it. He wanted it. He would often sit on his big rocking-horse, charging madly into space, riding toward luck.

When he had ridden to the end of his mad little journey, he would climb down and stand in front of his rocking-horse. He would stare into its face. Its red mouth was slightly open. Its big eye was wide and glassy-bright.

"Now!" he would silently command the horse. "Now, take me to where there is luck! Now take me!"

He knew the horse could take him to where there was luck, if only he forced it. He knew he could get there.

One day his mother and his Uncle Oscar came in when he was on one of his rides. He did not speak to them. He would speak to nobody when he was riding. His mother watched him with a scared look on her face.

At last, he suddenly stopped his gallop, and slid down.

"Well, I got there!" he said.

"Where did you get to?" asked his mother.

"Where I wanted to go," he flared back at her.

"That's right, son!" said Uncle Oscar. "Don't you stop till you get there. What's the horse's name?"

"He doesn't have a name," said the boy.

"Doesn't need one, huh?" said the uncle.

"Well, he has different names. He was called Sansovino last week."

"Sansovino, eh? He won the Ascot race. How did you know his name?"

"He always talks about horse races with Bassett," said Joan, the boy's sister.

The uncle was pleased to find that his nephew knew all the racing news. Bassett, the young gardener, had told him. Bassett lived for the racing events and the small boy lived with him.

The uncle went to his nephew and took him off for a ride in the car.

"Say, Paul, do you ever bet anything on a horse?" the uncle asked.

The boy watched the handsome man closely.

"Why? Do you think I shouldn't?" he asked.

"Not a bit of it! I thought you might give me a tip for the Lincoln race. Which horse do you think will win?"

"Daffodil," the boy answered.

"Daffodil! I doubt it, sonny. What about Mirza?"

"I only know the winner," said the boy. "That's Daffodil."

"Daffodil, eh?"

There was a pause. Daffodil was an unknown horse compared to the others.

"Uncle!"

"Yes, son?"

"You won't tell anyone else, will you?" said the boy. "I promised Bassett."

"Bassett be hanged! What's he got to do with it?"

"We're partners. We've been partners from the first. Uncle, he lent me my first five shillings that I lost. But you gave me that ten-shilling note. Then I started winning. So I thought you were lucky. You won't tell anyone else, will you?"

The boy looked at his uncle with those big, blue eyes and laughed uneasily.

"I'll keep your tip to myself. Daffodil, eh? How much are you putting on him?"

"All except twenty pounds," said the boy. "I keep that in reserve."

The uncle thought it a good joke.

"You keep twenty pounds in reserve, do you? What are you betting?"

"I'm betting three hundred," said the boy. "But it's between you and me, Uncle Oscar! Right?"

The uncle burst into laughter.

"It's between you and me all right," he said laughing. "But where's your three hundred?"

"Bassett keeps it for me. We're partners."

"You are, are you! And what is Basset putting on Daffodil?"

"He won't go quite as high as I do, I expect. Maybe he'll bet a hundred and fifty."

"What, pennies?" laughed the uncle.

"Pounds," said the child, with a surprised look. "Bassett keeps a bigger reserve than I do."

Between wonder and amusement, Uncle Oscar was silent. But he decided to take Paul with him to the Lincoln races.

"Now, son," he said. "I am putting twenty pounds on Mirza, and I'll put five for you on any horse you want. What's your pick?"

"Daffodil, uncle."

"No, not on Daffodil?"

"I would if it was my own five," said the child.

"Good. Right you are! A five for me and a five for you on Daffodil."

The child had never been to a race before, and his eyes were blue fire. He pursed his mouth tight, and watched.

81

A Frenchman just in front had put his money on Lancelot. Wild with excitement, he flayed his arms up and down, yelling "Lancelot! Lancelot" in his French accent.

Daffodil came in first, Lancelot second, Mirza third. Daffodil paid four to one.

"What am I to do with this money?" Uncle Oscar asked.

"We'll talk to Bassett," said the boy. "I expect I have fifteen hundred now. And I still have twenty in reserve. And now I have this twenty."

His uncle watched him for some time.

"Look here, son!" he said. "You don't mean it about Bassett, do you? Did he really win fifteen hundred for you?"

"Yes. But it's between you and me, uncle."

"All right, son! But I must talk to Bassett."

"We could all be partners, uncle. Only you'd have to promise not to let it go beyond us three. Bassett and I are lucky. And you must be lucky, too. It was your ten shillings I started winning with."

Uncle Oscar took both Bassett and Paul into Richmond Park for an afternoon. There, they talked.

"It's like this, sir," Bassett said. "Paul would get me talking about the races. I gave him five shillings to bet on one horse. We lost that one. But then you gave him ten shillings. The luck turned. We've been winning

pretty steady since then. Right, Paul?"

"We win when we're *sure*," the boy answered.

"But when are you sure?" Uncle Oscar asked Paul. Bassett answered for him, "It's as if he had it from heaven. Like Daffodil. That was sure."

"Did you bet on Daffodil?" asked Uncle Oscar.

"Yes," said Bassett.

"And my nephew? Did he bet too?"

Bassett was silent. He looked at Paul.

"I made twelve hundred. Didn't I, Bassett? I told uncle I was betting three hundred. And Daffodil paid four to one."

"That's right," said Bassett.

"But where's the money?" asked Uncle Oscar.

"I keep it safe, sir. Paul can have it whenever he wants it."

"It's amazing," said Uncle Oscar.

Uncle Oscar became a partner. For the next race, Paul was *sure* about Lively Spark. The horse was not expected to win. But the boy put one thousand pounds on him. Bassett put down five hundred. Oscar bet two hundred. Lively Spark came in first, paying ten to one.

Paul had made ten thousand pounds.

"You see," Paul said. "I was *sure* of him."

"What are you going to do with the money?" Uncle Oscar asked.

"I want to give it to mother. She says she has no luck. I thought if I was lucky, it would stop whispering."

"What would stop whispering?"

"Our house. I *hate* our house for whispering."

"What does it whisper?"

"It's always short of money."

"Yes, I know," said the uncle.

"I don't want mother to know I'm lucky, uncle."

"Why not?"

"She'd stop me."

"All right. We won't tell her. We'll get the money to her another way."

Uncle Oscar had a plan. He gave some of Paul's money to a lawyer. The lawyer called Paul's mother and told her that it was an inheritance. But even with the money, the house kept whispering: "There *must* be more money! There *must* be more money! *Now! Now! More money than ever!*"

Paul was afraid. He spent time with Bassett. Two races came and went and he had not been *sure* of either one. He lost four hundred pounds. The boy became wild-eyed and strange.

"Let it alone, Paul!" begged Uncle Oscar. But the boy ignored him.

"I've got to know for the Derby! I've *got* to know!" The child's eyes blazed with madness.

His mother, too, noticed how strange he had become. She wanted to send him to the shore for a rest. But he begged her, "Not before the Derby, mother. You don't need to worry about me." He looked at her without speaking. His heart held a secret. It was something not even Uncle Oscar or Bassett knew.

Paul's secret of secrets was his wooden horse. The horse stood in the boy's bedroom.

"You're too big for a rocking horse!" his mother had once said.

"He keeps me company," had been Paul's childish answer.

The Derby was drawing near. The boy grew more and more afraid. He hardly heard a word spoken to him. He grew thin. His eyes were strange. His mother feared for him. Sometimes she wanted to rush to him just to see if he was safe.

Three nights before the Derby, his mother went to a party in town. But some fear gripped her heart. She could hardly speak. She fought the feeling.

"The boy is all right," she kept telling herself. But the feeling was too strong and she left the party.

Back at the house, all was still. She went up to her son's room. She heard a noise which made her heart stand still. She stood outside the door, listening. There was a strange, heavy and yet not loud noise. It was a soundless noise. Something rushing and powerful. What was it? She ought to know. She felt she knew the noise. She knew what it was.

Yet, she could not place it. She couldn't say what it was. It just went on and on, like a madness.

Softly, filled with fear, she opened the door.

The room was dark. Yet in front of the window she saw something plunging back and forth. She turned on the light and saw her son madly riding the rocking-horse.

"Paul!" she cried. "What are you doing?"

"It's Malabar!" he screamed. His voice was strange. "It's Malabar!"

His eyes blazed at her for one second. Then he fell with a crash to the floor. His mother rushed to gather him up.

But he was unconscious. He remained that way all night, neither sleeping nor waking. Now and then, he cried out, "It's Malabar! It's Malabar!"

His mother sat by his side. "What does he mean by 'Malabar'?"

"I don't know!" said the boy's father.

"What does he mean, Oscar?" she asked her brother.

"It's one of the horses running in the Derby," was the answer.

Oscar spoke to Bassett and, in spite of himself, bet a thousand pounds on Malabar. The odds were fourteen to one.

On the third day, the boy's illness was worse. He tossed in his bed. His eyes were like blue stones. His mother felt that her heart had actually turned to stone.

That evening, Bassett came to see the boy.

"Paul," he whispered. "Malabar came in first all right. A clean win. I did as you told me. You've made over seventy thousand pounds, Paul. All together, you've got eighty thousand. Paul, Malabar won!"

The boy's eyes opened. "Malabar! Did you say 'Malabar'? Do you think I'm lucky, mother? Over eighty thousand pounds! I call that lucky. Don't you, mother? I knew. If I ride my horse till I'm *sure*, then it's all right. I never told you, mother. I can ride my horse and get there. Then I'm sure. Mother, did I ever tell you? I *am* lucky!"

"No, you never did," she said.

That night, Paul died.

Oscar spoke to Paul's mother. "Well," he said, "you're eighty thousand pounds richer. And a son poorer. But, poor devil, he's better off dead if he has to ride a rocking-horse to find a winner."

About the Author

D. H. Lawrence (1885-1930)

David Herbert Lawrence was born in Nottinghamshire, England, the son of a coal miner. He might have followed in his father's footsteps, except for poor health. Instead, Lawrence became a teacher and began to write. His first novel, *The White Peacock*, was published in 1911. Two years later, with the publication of *Sons and Lovers*, he became famous.

While Lawrence is best known as a novelist, he has written many excellent poems and short stories.

Focus on the Story

The **protagonist** is the hero of the story. The protagonist is usually the main character.

▶ **1.** The protagonist of this story is _____.
a. Paul
b. Uncle Oscar
c. Bassett

Point of View

▶ **2.** From whose point of view is "The Rocking-Horse Winner" told?
a. The story is told by Uncle Oscar. This is the first-person point of view.
b. The story is told by the mother. This is the first-person point of view.
c. The story is told by a narrator who is not a character in the story. This is the third-person point of view.

Characterization

▶ **3.** In this story, Paul's mother is characterized as _____.
a. a loving person
b. a very rich and beautiful woman
c. an unlucky person who couldn't love her children

4. Which word characterizes Paul?
a. troubled
b. carefree
c. happy

Motive

▶ **5.** What was Paul's reason for riding the rocking-horse?
a. He loved pretending that he was on a real horse.
b. The horse helped him discover who would win the races.
c. He didn't have any other toys.

Focus on the Language

Some words sound like the things they describe. When a word copies a sound, this is called **onomatopoeia.**

Examples:
- The snake *hissed* softly.
- We heard a *tapping* at the door.

Metaphor

Synonym

▶ **1.** Which sentence from "The Rocking-Horse Winner" contains an example of onomatopoeia?
a. There must be more money.
b. His heart held a secret.
c. He fell with a crash to the floor.

▶ **2.** Following are three descriptions of Paul's eyes. Which one is a metaphor?
a. His eyes were blazing madly.
b. His eyes were blue fire.
c. His eyes were like blue stones.

▶ **3.** A synonym for *luck* is _____.
a. *fortune*
b. *money*
c. *inheritance*

Write About It

Paul thought the rocking horse could take him to "luck." Paul's mother thought it was just a toy. How would Paul describe the horse to someone else? How would his mother describe it?

Write a paragraph describing the horse from Paul's or his mother's point of view. Begin with one of the following sentences:

- "The rocking horse was magical, and on it I could find luck."
- "It was just a toy and looked like any other rocking horse."

87

Midas and the Golden Touch

—A Greek Myth

Midas was a powerful king, both rich and greedy. On one occasion, he did a great favor for Bacchus, the god of wine. Bacchus offered Midas his choice of a reward. Midas answered at once. He asked that whatever he touched be turned into gold. Bacchus agreed, though he was sorry that Midas had not made a wiser choice.

Midas was eager to put his newly gained power to the test. He pulled a twig from a tree. The twig became gold in his hand. He picked up a stone; it turned to gold. He touched the grass. It, too, turned to gold.

Midas was overjoyed. Returning home, he ordered his servants to prepare a magnificent meal. But when he picked up some bread, it turned to gold. He lifted a glass of wine to his lips. But before he could taste it, it turned to gold.

Midas wished to free himself of his power. He hated the gift he had so recently desired. He raised his arms and begged and prayed for Bacchus to take away his deadly gift.

Bacchus showed pity. "Go," he said, "to the River Pactolus. There plunge yourself in. Wash away your greed and its punishment."

Midas did so. Hardly had he touched the waters, before the gold-making powers passed into them. The river sands changed into gold. And they remain golden to this day.

Focus on the Myth

A myth is a story that tries to explain the meaning of life. Myths are often about gods and goddesses who interact with people.

Moral

▶ **1.** What is the moral of this story?
a. There is more to life than riches.
b. Gold is more important than food.
c. You can't trust your friends.

Abstract Words

▶ **2.** Which words from the myth name ideas?
a. twig, gold, wine
b. greed, power, pity
c. river, stone, grass

Concrete Words

▶ **3.** Which words name things?
a. rich, greedy, favor
b. sorrow, power, reward
c. wine, bread, gold

The **climax** of a story is its turning point. In most stories, the climax is the event which causes a character to take some important action.

▶ **4.** The climax of "Midas and the Golden Touch" is the moment when _____.
a. Midas did a favor for Bacchus
b. Midas realized that he had made a mistake
c. Midas lost his power

Symbol

▶ **5.** Today, the name "Midas" refers to someone who makes money easily. When you say that a person has the "Midas touch," you mean that _____.
a. the person is very poor
b. gold is the most important thing to that person
c. everything that the person does makes money

89

Unit Review

Write your answers on a separate sheet of paper.

1. The protagonist of "The Monkey's Paw" is _____.
   - **a.** Herbert
   - **b.** Mr. White
   - **c.** Sergeant Morris

2. What is the setting of "The Pardoner's Tale"?
   - **a.** Flanders
   - **b.** Canterbury
   - **c.** a deserted town

3. In "The Pardoner's Tale" the main conflict is between _____.
   - **a.** a tavern owner and Death
   - **b.** an old man and Mother Earth
   - **c.** three friends

4. The theme of "The Rocking-Horse Winner" deals with _____.
   - **a.** luck and money
   - **b.** a search for Death
   - **c.** three wishes

5. The lesson of a story is its _____.
   - **a.** atmosphere
   - **b.** moral
   - **c.** conflict

6. Match each story with its time span.
   - **a.** The Monkey's Paw   a few months __
   - **b.** The Pardoner's Tale   about a week __
   - **c.** The Rocking-Horse Winner one day __

7. "Midas and the Golden Touch" is a _____.
   - **a.** poem
   - **b.** myth
   - **c.** work of nonfiction

Reviewing the Language

1. Which group of words from "The Monkey's Paw" best illustrates onomatopoeia?
   a. money, son, wish
   b. ticking, knock, howled
   c. paw, breakfast, nonsense

2. An example of slant rhyme is contained in which line from "The Pardoner's Tale"?
   a. You may have heard, he quickly kills without a word.
   b. Having tasted the poison which was inside, within a few minutes both men died.
   c. For he planned to work all night alone, carrying the gold back to his home.

3. Which words illustrate assonance?
   a. planned, work, eat
   b. alone, gold, home
   c. night, his, over

4. Here is a list of words. Which words are concrete? Which are abstract? Write "abstract" or "concrete" next to each word.

   luck _____   garden _____
   choice _____   table _____
   money _____   hope _____
   sky _____   window _____
   child _____   moon _____

Talking It Over

1. Each of the four selections in this unit deals with a "Double-Edged Dream." Think about Mr. White, Paul, Midas, and the three friends in "The Pardoner's Tale." What dream did each of these characters have? How did these dreams prove to be "double-edged"?

2. Which character do you believe most deserved to have his dream come true? Who was least deserving?

3. The quotation at the beginning of this unit is: "If a man could have half his wishes, he would double his troubles." Do you believe this is true? Which characters found it to be so?

91

About the Poets

HANNAH KAHN (1911-   )

Hannah Kahn was born in New York City, but she now makes her home in Florida. She has written hundreds of poems and has received more than twenty-five awards for her poetry. Because of illness, Kahn's education was interrupted. But at the age of fifty, she again began to take classes, one night a week, at Miami Dade College. Twelve years later, at age sixty-two, she received her degree. Today Kahn lectures about poetry at colleges and universities and also conducts poetry workshops. She is the poetry review editor for *The Miami Herald*.

MARGARET WALKER (1915-   )

Margaret Walker has worked as a newspaper reporter, social worker, magazine editor, and college professor. Born in Birmingham, Alabama, she received her Ph.D. at the University of Iowa and is now a member of the Department of English at Jackson State College in Mississippi. In addition to her many poems, Walker has also written a novel, *Jubilee,* as well as several nonfiction works. She has won numerous awards for her writing, including a Fullbright fellowship in 1971.

Glossary

Abstract Words—words that name ideas that *cannot* be touched, heard, smelled, seen, or tasted; for example, *courage, joy, friendship*

Alliteration—the repetition of consonant sounds; for example, He told a tale of terror.

Allusion—a reference to some person, place, thing, or event that a reader is likely to recognize

Antonyms—words that are opposite in meaning; for example, *fast* is an antonym for *slow*.

Assonance—when vowel sounds are repeated; for example, *hide* and *wise*

Atmosphere—the overall feeling that a story produces in a reader

Author's Purpose—the reason the author wrote a story. An author's purpose may be to entertain, inform, teach, or convince.

Author's Style—the way a writer uses language; the choice of words and the arrangement of words and sentences

Author's Viewpoint—the way an author feels about the subject matter

Autobiography—a type of literature in which a person tells about his or her own life

Biography—a type of literature in which a writer tells about someone else's life

Call Number—the identification number printed on the spine of a library book (**See Dewey Decimal System.**)

Character—a person in a story

Character Development—the change in a character from beginning to end of a story